THE ROBOT AND AUTOMATION ALMANAC 2021

THE FUTURIST INSTITUTE

Edited by Jason Schenker
Chairman of The Futurist Institute

THE ROBOT AND AUTOMATION ALMANAC - 2021

THE FUTURIST INSTITUTE

EDITED BY JASON SCHENKER

ISBN: 978-1-946197-68-9 *Paperback*
          978-1-946197-71-9 *Ebook*

For futurists everywhere.

 THE FUTURIST INSTITUTE

CONTENTS

CONTENTS

CONTENTS

FROM THE FUTURIST INSTITUTE

So much has changed in the past year. The disruption of COVID-19 has created a greater need to think strategically about the future than ever before. It is my hope that *The Robot and Automation Almanac - 2021* helps you consider the future in this way.

On behalf of The Futurist Institute, I want to acknowledge and thank all of the contributors to *The Robot and Automation Almanac - 2021*. As in the past three years, we have an amazing cohort of contributors in the fields of robots, automation, and AI this year.

Thank you to Michael Walton, Kevin Paramore, Brandon Coats, Chris Lingamfelter, Djamila Amimer, Kyle Palko, Ragu Athinarayanan, Xiumin Diao, Balamurugan Balakreshnan, Matthew Frazier, Patrick Davison, Cecilia Boström, Garrett Place, Kaleb Steinhauer, Micah Green, Steven LaFevers, Nawfal Patel, Jacob Sotiriadis, Robert Handfield, and Daniel Stanton. I am humbled by this list of amazing authors!

The contributions of these leaders will help shape the vision for robots, automation, and AI in the year to come — and beyond. Their words and expectations for "the big thing" in the year ahead have created an important vision of the future.

Without them, this book would never have happened. Their visions of the future are both exciting and valuable.

I also want to thank parties who have helped out by providing recommendations for potential contributors, including MHI — the Material Handling Industry group — with which my financial market research firm, Prestige Economics, has a long-standing relationship.

Additionally, I need to thank the individuals who have provided support and feedback to this project, especially Nawfal Patel, who helped managed the process so that this book could come to fruition. And, of course, Kerry Ellis has my gratitude for designing such a wonderful cover for the almanac.

It is my personal pleasure to have been involved in this undertaking. The robotics, automation, and AI industries are still very new, but they are becoming more important. And it is with great pleasure that The Futurist Institute is able to support the companies in these industries with this almanac.

I founded The Futurist Institute to help strategists, analysts, and executives become futurists in October 2016; we recently began our fifth year of operations. In the wake of the COVID-19 pandemic, our year has been off to a busy start.

With the inaugural edition of *The Robot and Automation Almanac* in 2018, The Futurist Institute created an invaluable tool for professionals, individuals, and investors seeking to understand the implications of robots and automation for their personal, professional, and investing lives.

We have similarly high expectations for how *The Robot and Automation Almanac - 2021* will presage changes in the year ahead, and that it will also help professionals think strategically about a variety of potential changes in the wake of the COVID-19 disruption that has dominated 2020.

The transition from the information age into the automation age is underway. Thank you for being a part of this dynamic shift.

Welcome to the future! ~

Jason Schenker
Chairman of The Futurist Institute
Editor of *The Robot and Automation Almanac*

THE YEAR AHEAD AND BEYOND

Jason Schenker

- Chairman of The Futurist Institute -

Every year the topics of robots, automation, and artificial intelligence become more important. These topics became even more critical against the backdrop of the COVID-19 pandemic. And during the pandemic automation in the supply chain became both more critical and more visible than ever.

When I took MBA courses in the early 2000s, the words supply chain were barely uttered. But as a result of the COVID-19 pandemic, and the associated shortages of paper products and concerns about food, now everyone from grannies to little kids knows what supply chain is.

This is the fourth edition of *The Robot and Automation Almanac*, and supply chain-related automation features prominently in this edition — as has been the case in each of the previous editions.

We are on the verge of the age of automation. And COVID-19 pushed that automation forward.

While automation has been driven by convenience, operational efficiency, and economic incentives, the pandemic engendered necessity.

Going into 2020, there were domestic and global macroeconomic risks. And the trade war was still raging. These were the biggest risks that threatened to weigh on business investment, including hindering some technological investments.

Then COVID-19 broke out, and that changed the year entirely. For many industries, COVID-19 was devastating. But supply chain, automation, robots, robotics, contactless technologies, big data, AI, and remote work have seen a surge of adoption, development, and growth.

What's next for robots, automation, and AI in 2021? This is the question that our contributors have answered in this book.

The year ahead is going to be one of significant expansion in robots and automation. It will be a year of advancements across the technological gamut that allows for digital transformation to be more complete and integrated for business operations as well as our own personal lives.

In addition to their contributions, we are also grateful for all of the images our contributors granted us permission to use in this book.

The history of robots and automation is being written now.

When people look back a decade from now, they will want to know how robots and automation evolved. They will want to understand how robots and AI became more integrated.

They will wish they had known more when it was happening.

They will wish they had read *The Robot and Automation Almanac* as it was happening. ~

Jason Schenker is the Chairman of The Futurist Institute.

THE FUTURE IS FOR FUTURISTS

Jason Schenker

- Chairman of The Futurist Institute -

People define the word futurist differently. I consider myself an applied futurist, with a practical, sober, and data-driven approach to the future. In my world, and for those of us at The Futurist Institute, a futurist is someone who looks at the trends of the past and the data of the present to formulate expectations of the future. Normally, futurists operate in a time window beyond that of economists and financial market analysts. In other words, futurists have usually made predictions about trends, technology, and markets in the 10-year window or so.

But that all changed in 2020.

Against the backdrop of COVID-19, the need for futurists — people who have built careers making forecasts in a fog of uncertainty — became prominent in 2020. Plus, the window of analysis for future scenarios became compressed and the notion of futurist as someone who thinks about Star Trek-like technology changed drastically as near-term forecasting became exceptionally difficult.

In many ways, ubiquitous uncertainty forced the issue, to the point that the only solution for prediction in such a wild environment became engaging futurists who use a series of frameworks and scenario analysis to identify levers of opportunity and risk, as well as drivers of disruption and change.

This approach informed the content and scenarios presented in my best-selling book *The Future After COVID*. That book and related content also led to collaboration with the U.S. Air Force Strategic Foresight and Futures Branch out of the Pentagon, which is headed by Lt. Col. Jacob Sotiriadis, who also contributed to this almanac.

The June 2020 report resulting from my collaboration with the U.S. air force was the *Global Futures Report: Alternative Futures of Geopolitical Competition in a Post-COVID-19 World*. My section was titled "The Future Nexus of Supply Chains and National Security."

This unclassified Pentagon futures report can be downloaded from The Futurist Institute website in its entirety at: http://www.futuristinstitute.org/pentagon-report/

Looking Back to Look Ahead
One common aphorism that most economists subscribe to is that "this time is never different." In many ways, I find this is a useful notion when thinking about technology as a futurist as well. Many forms of new tech are reincarnations or more advanced permutations of long-standing forms of technology that usually have a long historical trend of adaptation and advancement behind them.

It's why people often say that "what's old is new again."

When I founded The Futurist Institute in 2016, the goal was to help leaders plan for uncertainty engendered by disruptions in technology and trends. One of our most important deliverables has been this almanac, which is why this is the fourth annual edition of *The Robot and Automation Almanac*.

While many futurists operate in the 10-year period or later, we have always considered it valuable to analyze the near-term dynamics of the year ahead as well as the period through the decade ahead and the period past that decade. For many, one year ahead might not seem "future" enough. But with the thought leaders, executives, and experts contributing to this almanac, we have been able to craft an informed view of the world in the next 12 months.

Last year's big themes included macroeconomic risks, physical automation in controlled environments, a push for efficiencies, a march toward more effective operations, ethical challenges, and environmental needs. And of course, the 2020 edition of *The Robot and Automation Almanac* also included the prescient article that I co-authored with my colleague Nawfal Patel on the subject of remote work. Talk about a prediction for "the big thing" in the year ahead.

Now, looking ahead to 2021, I see a world in transition, struggling to emerge from pandemic and regain a sense of normalcy, while still being split by two polar opposite instincts.

On the one hand, many companies, organizations, and individuals will likely seek to hold on to the convenience and operational gains achieved through the forced digital transformation that occurred in the throes of the initial waves of the COVID-19 pandemic.

On the other hand, there will likely be many companies that try to wind the clock back to a simpler pre-transformation time before COVID. But that bygone time may also just be gone. The notion that all workers will just stream back into offices to again live commute-ridden, maskless existences just seems too far-fetched to believe.

The third way forward, where companies have flexible space that both reduces overhead and still allows for some workers to be in the office some of the time seems more likely. It has also been an operational norm for many management consulting firms for well over a decade. It was the case when I started with McKinsey in 2007.

This begs the question: Why wouldn't consulting firms that advise corporations on operational best practices recommend adopting the remote working model that those same consulting firms have used for some time?

The answer may lie in education. In fact, for some time, the most critical deciding factor for remote work was education. In general, the more education required and the more professional the role, the greater the chance that the job had gained remote workers in the past decade and a half.

But COVID-19 became a true inflection point for remote work.

Data from the U.S. BLS indicate that the vast majority of workers with advanced degrees were working remotely for part of 2020 because of COVID-19. This can be seen in the figure below.

Plus, that data does not include the percent of workers with advanced degrees that were working remotely before COVID. In other words, in the United States, perhaps as many as 90 percent of workers with advanced degrees were working remotely for part of May 2020.

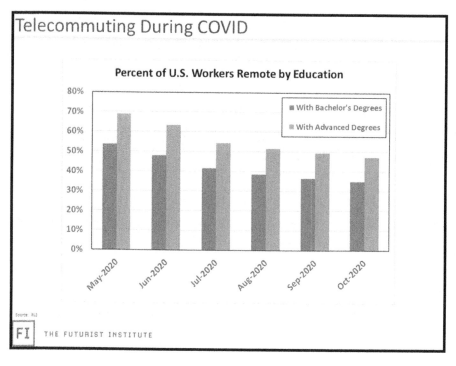

The majority of U.S. workers with advanced degrees worked remotely because of COVID-19 at times in 2020.[1]

Workers with advanced degrees, high levels of education, and significant professional skills are in short supply — and their unemployment rate is always the lowest across education cohorts. In other words, this is a group with leverage when it comes to their employability.

Looking ahead, U.S. BLS data also offer a potential warning.

Before COVID-19, corporations were mustering resources to win the war for talent. Now, as a result of COVID, that talent has seen a major shift in their working environments in the year ahead and beyond. As the world lurches forward to some semblance of normalcy, corporate operating environments may be forever changed. And the trend to remote work may be irreversible.

The push to wrangle highly educated workers back into florescent-light-filled cube farms — as well as beautiful Class-A office high rises — is a battle that can be won, but only at the expense of losing the war for talent.

Labor markets have historically been local markets, and remote work has caused a phase shift that makes the entire global labor market into a local market. This is true for both employees and employers. Companies that embrace remote work will be able to turn the global market into their own local labor market, with greater chances to attract and retain the best professionals.

For those with the strongest background, best skills, and advanced degrees, leverage to access more jobs has also just gone up — despite slack in the U.S. and global labor markets.

Companies that embrace the change to remote work will win an increasingly global war for talent. Those that try to wind back the clock and force a return to the office, may find fewer hands on deck just as a fuller economic and labor market recovery takes hold.

The big takeaway here is that remote work is not just a temporary solution to help the world muddle through during a pandemic. Remote work has been a trend that started before the last recession, and it is here to stay. The companies that embrace this reality will be poised to win big in the year ahead. And those that ignore it run the risk of losing the war for talent. ~

ENDNOTE

1. https://www.bls.gov/cps/effects-of-the-coronavirus-covid-19-pandemic.htm#table1

Jason Schenker is the Chairman of The Futurist Institute. He has worked remotely since 2007, both at McKinsey and Company as a Risk Specialist and running his own companies since 2009.

ONE UNIVERSE FOR ALL ROBOTS

Michael Walton

- Microsoft Industry Solutions Executive -

Bots currently exist in a fractured, divided universe.

They operate on various platforms, with varied ways in which they communicate. Many of them may be able to receive and relay information but are unable to communicate with each other. This poses scalability problems for companies looking to expand their automation capabilities.

But there is more.

The universe of bots is not static. There are many robots in use now, but so many more will be added in the future. Plus, there are legacy bots. Over time, the communication challenges will only grow, as the number of bots increases exponentially.

In order for companies to fully optimize their operations and derive value from the automated solutions in their facilities and across their organizations, these bots on varied platforms and of varied ages need to be able to communicate.

Bots have to be able to receive communications, send communications, and communicate with each other in a universal way. Without the ability to communicate in an increasingly diverse world of bots, the efficiencies we might expect to gain from automation and the use of robots could slow sharply.

That's the exact opposite goal of investing in and deploying automated solutions. It is exactly for this reason that the greatest challenge for 2021 will be creating one universe of bots.

There needs to be a system that allows all of the bots to coexist, to allow remote access as well as remote control — and to facilitate communication across all directions. It's something we've been calling BYOB — or Bring Your Own Bot.

The notion is that universal communication leads to democratization and allows for general purpose bot use in the same way that all smartphones can communicate with each other and with other devices across a number of different communication mediums and brands, whether the devices are Google Pixels, Apple iPhones, Samsung Androids, RIM BlackBerry phones, or Microsoft Surface devices. Plus, all of those can communicate with landline phones, analog cell phones, pay phones, and older flip phones that are still in use. They can even receive calls from any old rotary phones that are still out there.

The same is true, of course, for personal computers. These devices can communicate across networks and applications regardless of brand, operating system, internet service provider, or age.

This will also be true of bots in the future. In fact, it is happening now — and will accelerate in the year ahead. It is the single-most pressing issue in the world of robotics — especially for industrial use cases. The future of bots is one universe. But for that to happen, a common ground needs to be laid out, and the barriers preventing smooth and seamless bot communication and interface need to be broken down, so that the bot universe of the future looks a lot like the universe of phones and devices of today.

It will not happen overnight. But big strides are coming in the years ahead. And 2021 will be a year in which we move the needle in shaping one universe for all bots. ~

Michael Walton is Director and Industry Solutions Executive at Microsoft, where he is helping discrete manufacturing companies to digitally transform.

A PRACTICAL APPROACH TO ROBOTICS IMPLEMENTATION

Kevin Paramore

- Emerging Technology Commercialization Manager at
Yale Materials Handling Corporation -

Introduction

Supply chains have warmed up to the idea that robotic solutions make real business sense for warehouse and manufacturing operations. While some may have eyed robotics as laden with future potential, for many, underlying trends and unexpected events have accelerated their timeline for warehouse robotics from an opportunity for tomorrow to an essential for today.

Labor costs and challenges persist, customer expectations continue to raise the bar for performance, and social distancing brought on by the COVID-19 pandemic has introduced fresh hurdles to the already demanding task of staffing supply chain operations.[1,2]

Modern robotics can spare operations the major investment of installing fixed infrastructure, with autonomous navigation technology enabling relatively quick deployment. But implementation still comes with numerous questions, from ROI and safety to IT, integration, and planning. As facilities fast-track robotic adoption in response to the tyranny of the urgent and to position themselves for long-term competitive advantage, careful preparation can smooth the path to successful implementation.

Evaluating Your Operation as a Candidate for Robotics

The first step to successful robotics implementation is understanding where and how your operation best stands to benefit — essentially qualifying your operation. Robotics are not a one-size fits all solution, so setting the stage for a tailored approach requires working with a trusted partner to first assess which applications in your facility are best suited for automation. This process covers the environment in which robotics would operate, the types of tasks they must complete, and characteristics of the loads they must handle. The following characteristics typically indicate an operation is well-suited for mobile robotics:

- Challenges sourcing and retaining labor
- Two-, three-, and four-shift operations
- Repetitive tasks
- Long horizontal runs or vertical movements
- Indoor work setting
- Clean, smooth, dry floors
- Ramps or inclines less than 3 degrees

Another important step is defining success — in other words, what level of return is necessary to make the investment worthwhile, and over what timeframe? The all-in burdened labor cost against the cost of augmenting operations with robotics is core to answering this question. But hourly labor rates are not the full story. For example, in industries like warehousing where average employee turnover is high, finding and replacing employees involves considerable time and expense, while damage to the facility, equipment, and product due to operator error can all add up.[3,4]

Making the Numbers Work

Is a significant CapEx budget a necessary prerequisite for automation projects? Not necessarily, as rental and lease options that essentially provide "robots as a service" would suggest. Return on robotics investments can also come more quickly than many operations may think possible. How soon? Most two to three shift applications can see a fairly common ROI timetable of less than two years.

When automating processes and calculating the associated payback, direct labor savings are obvious wins, with expenses like hourly wages, overtime, and holiday pay rising to the top. But automation drives savings in other indirect ways by drastically reducing costs associated with retraining and re-education, workers' compensation, lost time due to illness or injury, and long-term wage increases. The Material Handling and Logistics U.S. Roadmap 2.0 supports this, stating that "automation will likely continue to become less costly, while wages and benefits for human workers will increase over time."

Enabling Successful Implementation

New technology can only be effective insofar as it is accepted, so introducing employees to their new robotic co-workers is an important step and opportunity. Proactively inform teams about any changes to the workplace involving robotics. Share how workflows will change and reinforce the meaningful benefits for your employees — less repetitive work, allowing them to focus on more engaging value-added responsibilities.[5]

As with all tools, proper safety training and protocols are essential. Train all employees on proper procedures for working around robots and collaborating with them in cobotic workflows. Robotic lift trucks offer a unique capability for operator interaction, as they can be switched from automatic to manual mode. This dual-mode capability enables operations to adapt to unexpected circumstances, with employees able to simply engage the controls and take control just as they would standard lift truck equipment.

IT is also an important consideration. While integrating robotics software with the facility's WMS is not a requirement, it can enable more seamless operation and tightly managed workflows. Enlisting IT early in the process helps determine requirements or can reveal any potential capacity issues that could make deferring WMS integration to a later phase a more attractive approach. Robotic lift trucks, for instance, can handle basic point-to-point transportation tasks without requiring such significant software integration, enabling operations to get robotics up and running quickly and more simply.

Navigation technology is another important consideration for startup cost and time. While traditional automatic guided vehicles (AGVs) require guidance infrastructure to be installed, mobile robotics do not share this requirement, instead using existing structural features like walls, columns, and racks. They require a "walk" of the facility to create an internal map to reference against what they see in real time to self-locate and navigate.

Beyond Initial Implementation: Keeping the Future in Mind
With fluctuating demand and a constantly evolving warehouse environment, automation investments must have the flexibility to meet the challenges of today — and tomorrow. For example, robots that can be easily re-programmed and re-deployed in different settings can easily adapt to renovations, new workflows, and other changes as business dictates. But the adaptability of individual robotics investments is only a piece of a complete plan for the future.

Beyond the initial robotics investment, operations can think of automation as a phased journey.

Both the challenges that drive businesses to look for automated solutions and the capability and cost of robotic technology keep evolving. Incorporating robotics and automation into long-term strategic planning discussions can position operations for future competitive advantage while also providing a framework to adapt should conditions change — accelerating timelines or adjusting plans to fit the needs of the business. ~

Robotic lift truck moving pallets in a warehouse.

ENDNOTES

1. https://www.bls.gov/news.release/jolts.t16.htm
2. https://project44.showpad.com/share/tfGo7Eh7700A502hrkowb
3. https://www.bls.gov/news.release/jolts.t16.htm
4. https://www.peoplekeep.com/blog/employee-retention-the-real-cost-of-losing-an-employee
5. https://www.prnewswire.com/news-releases/automation-is-making-work-more-human-global-research-reveals-300714154.html

Kevin Paramore works as part of Yale's emerging technology team to provide problem-solving solutions that leverage the latest technologies, available through national account and dealer sales channels. He has over 15 years of experience leading sales teams and a bachelor's degree from East Carolina University.

WHAT CAN AI DO IN THE WAREHOUSE?

Brandon Coats

- Global Product Manager of Robotics and Vision at Material Handling Systems, Inc. -

What is AI? And What Can it do in the Warehouse?

For operations looking to automate more complex tasks, AI is the ultimate enabler.

Artificial intelligence. In popular culture, AI brings to mind images of the dystopian reality of the matrix or the docile-turned-destructive humanoids of *I, Robot*. But in today's reality, AI is gaining traction for less sinister reasons.

The real-world application of AI is, predictably, more practical. Businesses can think of AI as a great enabler, capable of automating processes that have long been targets for automation but presented too much complexity for contemporary technology.

For example, past technology could successfully automate repetitive, predictable processes in manufacturing but struggled to be effective with the variety of workflows and items found in e-commerce distribution centers.

By contrast, AI can provide visual perception to identify and classify individual items without explicit programming. AI can be used to tackle problems of path planning, dexterity, and grasp by learning from previous pick attempts or by supervised learning. This combination enables robotics to handle highly variable work, such as singulating various parcels for downstream automation or picking items for individual e-commerce orders.

Looking Under the Hood of Contemporary AI
Current AI is enabled by a combination of disparate technologies continually merging. In warehousing, this includes robots, grippers, sensors, and software. This consolidation is driven by the ability to digitize various information and Moore's Law, the observation that we can expect the speed and capability of computers to increase consistently, doubling every year or two. Exponential growth is a hallmark of these technologies, as evidenced by smartphones of today having over a million times more memory and more than 100,000 times the processing power of the computer used in the Apollo 11 mission.[1]

Neural networks are foundational in today's AI. Much like a digitized brain, an input triggers an output and is in turn received as input to other neurons.

In practice, there may be hundreds of thousands to millions of "neurons" in a model, each of which recognizes specific patterns within the dataset at various levels of abstraction from micro to macro. Deep neural networks consist of ten layers or greater in which each layer serves as one level of abstraction between the input and output, and they are triggered at detection of trained objects.

What can these deep neural networks do? Convolutional neural networks, for example, are commonly applied to analyzing visual imagery and can pick up patterns and trends from very granular levels, like texture, color differentiation, and more, up to big-picture views like net shapes.

But neural networks have existed for decades. Why the current renaissance? The missing link for decades was the absence of computers with enough computing power to leverage them. At the beginning of the 2010s, researchers learned how to leverage consumer-grade gaming GPUs, which drop predictably in cost from year to year, to greatly enhance capacity and speed when developing neural networks.[2] GPUs had been growing in power and cost performance driven by the need to visualize and display information on screens at rates fast enough to be perceived as continuous by the human eye. The key was highly parallelized calculations distributed to as many compute cores as possible. This enabled technical feasibility for responsive neural networks as they are highly parallelizable.

The advent of sensors generating vast amounts of data is another key development in enabling today's AI.

Artificial intelligent robot on display at R&D event.

Before neural networks and deep learning, collecting data was possible, but putting it to work was another story as software was simply not up to par with human recognition of patterns in complex datasets. Neural networks provide such an outlet, as training them requires a tremendous amount of data, giving organizations productive ways to leverage what they collect.

Powerful Problem Solving

When applying AI to solve problems and deliver market-ready solutions, businesses can leverage scale, using as many neural networks as they desire.

One example of an application in material handling that has matured for commercial application is vision-based robotic picking. Essentially, AI comes with the ability to identify objects within an image, providing the basis for robots to detect the presence and location of objects to coordinate grasping for desired handling operations.

Another important note about neural networks is their ability to expedite the problem-solving process. In engineering, non-linear problems are the types of challenges in which the output does not change in proportion to the input — the aforementioned visual identification task is one example among others that the human brain is well-suited to handle. When mathematical functions begin to mimic what the brain does, applying complex models to neural networks can enable effective non-linear problem solving — without requiring high levels of programming and heavy lifting by engineering resources. In a no-code programming future not too far from present, simply dragging and dropping widgets on an intuitive user interface will allow people not otherwise skilled in programming to create a powerful neural network to solve any non-linear problem of their choosing.[3,4]

Why the Warehouse?

This current breed of AI is especially well-suited for warehouse environments due to the variability of workpieces — such as bagged items, corrugate cases, or other types of packages — that the robot handles. The vision capability offered by the neural networks provides output on par with almost anything a person can see.

Most importantly, the capability provides information regarding target selection, location, and depth when selecting one workpiece out of many.

As a worker reaches out to grab an individual item, the brain calculates the depth to grasp and bring it back — this depth calculation happens while the reach is in progress, not as a separate process prior to target selection.

This approach can be replicated by AI, using visual information to define the target, calculate depth, plan its path, and then grasp the workpiece sequentially and soon in real time. Robots connected to the digital warehouse will anticipate future orders and be able to optimize current orders to bring the warehouse into singular harmonious motion. Taking it all in, robots need context just as an operator working an assembly line would. Just as operators develop instinct — the subconscious ability to compress, encode and simplify data in our surroundings — so will robots.

For warehouses, this evolution matters due to performance and adaptability. The nature of work in e-commerce-driven environments revolves around speed to meet fast delivery requirements, and the ability to handle a wide range of inventory. As labor becomes more expensive and difficult to source, logistics operations need automated alternatives capable of performing what they would expect from manual processes — and AI is an enabler of solutions capable of doing just that.

Continued Evolution

Today's AI is merging exponential technologies and is set to become increasingly powerful and capable as these technologies continue to merge and advance. This compounding extends beyond the traditional paradigm of Moore's Law improving computer technology every year as well as sensors getting smaller and more potent. AI advances at an exceptional rate due to the exponential growth across individual technologies which in turn is merged by novel software.

Keep an eye on AI in the warehousing and distribution space. If 2020 was the year that vision perception crossed the threshold into widespread economic viability, then we should expect 2021 to be marked by a deployment of products employing multiple neural networks aimed at enabling groundbreaking new capabilities that can in turn enable businesses to better serve customers and do so more profitably. ~

Automated robot sorting packages using AI.

ENDNOTES

1. https://www.realclearscience.com/articles/2019/07/02/your_mobile_phone_vs_apollo_11s_guidance_computer_111026.html
2. https://ark-invest.com/wrights-law/
3. https://www.youtube.com/watch?v=jlks6J78R-8
4. https://www.fastcompany.com/90157777/this-is-the-worlds-first-graphical-ai-interface

Brandon Coats is responsible for developing material handling systems that leverage robotics, sensors, machine vision, AI, and other exponential technologies.

THE 2021 MOMENT OF TRUTH FOR DISTRIBUTION CENTERS

Chris Lingamfelter

- Vice President of Sales at 6 River Systems -

Using Robotic Automation to Combat Disruption and Uncertainty in Supply Chains

The biggest make or break challenge for supply chains in 2021 will be how they adapt to a changing pandemic environment. While availability and distribution of a coronavirus vaccine are on the horizon in 2021, we're still far from being out of the woods.

There are some indications that the current flu season in the Northern Hemisphere might mean the pandemic will be worse than yet experienced, which raises a few important questions. Assuming healthcare workers, the elderly and others most at risk will be the first to receive the vaccine, when will it become widely available to all? How do we, in the business of order fulfillment, prepare for the dramatic and continued uptick in online shopping?

Will we have a holiday peak on top of a pandemic peak? How will this impact the processing of returns? Will employees be willing to come to work in distribution centers? How can we best ensure their safety during this dangerous and uncertain time?

Continued Talent Challenges

Although there are many unknowns to wrestle with, there's plenty we do know about warehouse operations. First, pandemic aside, the majority of roles within a distribution center are challenging jobs, involving tedious and repetitive tasks, from picking and packing to receiving and shipping. Attracting and retaining employees can be particularly difficult, especially as competing operations bump up their hourly rates for these roles.

However, to run sustainable, profitable businesses, warehouse operators must keep a close eye on payroll which, after transportation, is often their biggest expense. So, the key is to stay competitive with those pay rates without overdoing it, provide a safe work environment, and invest in automation solutions that work with people and help to increase their productivity, and potentially job satisfaction.

Distribution From a Distance

Let's say the wages being offered are in the ballpark of what warehouse workers would consider. Next on the checklist is safety, which is not only important to the staff and considered by job applicants, if mishandled it could mean shutting down a portion or even an entire operation until it's all clear to return. With coronavirus being a major concern today and for the foreseeable future, actions taken inside a warehouse to minimize and eliminate risk are of utmost importance.

Although it's a measure that's tough to swallow for warehouse operators, limiting the number of people inside a facility is one way to lessen the amount of potential germs transmitted between employees both through the air and on surfaces. But a work from home mandate isn't possible when it comes to most jobs in a distribution center. The physical nature of warehouse work means an on-site presence is essential for getting online orders processed, packaged, and shipped. Sure, there's talk of lights-out warehouses where humans aren't part of the equation. Usually such complete automation is out-of-bounds financially and so inflexible it's not practical. Experts agree that the most effective mix consists of people assisted by robots for maximum efficiency and productivity, thereby accelerating the flow of material handling and fulfillment.[1,2,3]

What to Consider

When it comes to robotic automation solutions facilitating the picking process in fulfillment centers, a number of options have proven to be effective and increasingly popular. And while these types of robots have been deployed around the world since well before the pandemic began, they're now being seen as an ideal solution for giving people the space they need to stay safe. Here are a few to consider as a way to minimize the transmission of germs among fulfillment center employees.

1. Autonomous Mobile Robots (AMRs) — In a traditional warehouse, workers spend hours during a shift simply walking the floor to gather items for an individual order. With an AMR doing the cross-warehouse travel, people are able to steer clear of each other, crossing paths far less than in an AMR-less, non-automated facility.

Another type of AMR travels ahead of a human picker, leading him or her to inventory within the aisles of a fulfillment center, providing signals as to what items need to be collected for each order. Like many pandemic-modified supermarkets, the aisles of a warehouse can be set up for one-way traffic, enabling a collaborative robot and its human counterpart to steer clear of other people.

These human-assist AMRs can stay with the same worker throughout a pick run instead of being touched by multiple workers. And when it's time to start another pick run, the surfaces of an AMR can be sanitized to prevent the passing of germs to the next warehouse worker to use the robot.

It is also possible to establish hard picking zone boundaries to limit the number of pickers in a physical work area. One third party logistics provider hard limited each aisle to one picker, effectively eliminating pickers being near one another.

2. Robotic Piece-Picking Solutions — Robotic piece-picking solutions take on the task of selecting an item from one bin and placing it in another bin containing a variety of SKUs for an individual order. Imagine a human doing this monotonous work for an entire shift. Errors are bound to happen, and each touch adds to the cost of fulfillment. A robotic piece-picking solution, on the other hand, is accurate, dependable and over time reduces costs involved with fulfilling an order. Furthermore, each picking robot replaces a human that could introduce, carry, or contract the virus.

With online shopping rapidly on the rise, having reliable piece-pickers in place is critical for getting orders out the door, accurately and on time. And now, with coronavirus, it's important to limit the number of employees coming in contact with each other inside distribution centers. Robotic piece-picking solutions help to accomplish that, while also taking on these hard-to-fill, monotonous jobs.

3. Goods-to-Picker Robotics — Goods-to-picker (G2P) robotic systems bring items directly to an individual, thereby reducing foot traffic and helping to minimize the amount of people coming in contact with each other in a fulfillment center.

Certain automated storage and retrieval systems (ASRS) have other benefits, such as taking advantage of typically untapped vertical space in warehouses. However, goods-to-picker systems are usually quite costly and inflexible.

Another type of G2P solution you might be familiar with are the robotic shuttles originally developed by Kiva Systems and acquired by Amazon for its own fulfillment center needs back in 2012. These mobile bots transport shelves of items from various areas of a warehouse to human pickers; Such a system is flexible, but costly as 8 to 12 robots are required to support each picker.

The Case for Investing in Robotics and Automation
If this too shall pass with a COVID vaccine on the way, why invest in robotics and automation?

If we take an optimistic view and speculate that a vaccine is designed, approved, and widely distributed in 2021, then is it really worth investing in robotic automation if there's light at the end of the tunnel for social distancing requirements?

Or, if a less optimistic view is taken, then the need for warehouse workers to keep their distance could continue for another year or more. Let's hope not.

But in the interest of safety and the expectation that online shopping habits will continue to trend upward for the 2021 peak season, it could be a very wise move to ensure that our DCs are optimally automated with robotic solutions. And as supply chain professionals, it's our business to ensure that our facilities are set up for success in the coming months, years and beyond. Employees are depending on it. And so are customers.

A global pandemic notwithstanding, the need for speed, accuracy and flexibility will always be priorities when it comes to meeting and exceeding customer expectations. Whether we're in a pandemic or not, automating with collaborative robots is the key to increasing worker productivity and satisfaction, ensuring operational efficiency, and creating customer loyalty. ~

ENDNOTES

1. https://www.mmh.com/article/
    automated_warehouses_on_the_path_to_lights_out
2. https://www.dcvelocity.com/articles/28079-it-s-lights-out-in-the-warehouse
3. https://www2.deloitte.com/us/en/pages/manufacturing/articles/
    autonomous-robots-supply-chain-innovation.html

Chris Lingamfelter, a 30-year supply chain technologist, has helped build some of the most exciting supply chain tech companies including 6 River Systems, Kiva (now Amazon Robotics), Dematic, Intelligrated, Manhattan Associates, and Exeter Software. He is VP Sales at 6 River Systems, the leading provider of collaborative mobile supply chain robots.

ARTIFICIAL INTELLIGENCE IN A POST-COVID WORLD: 2021 AND BEYOND

Djamila Amimer

- CEO and Founder, Mind Senses Global -

COVID-19 has impacted every aspect of our lives including the way we do business. In fact, according to a recent survey by McKinsey, COVID has accelerated companies' digital transformation journeys.[1] In a post-COVID world, there will be an even-greater acceleration of AI adoption by enterprises.

AI business applications will be centred around automating tasks, forecasting supply disruptions, and enhancing customer behavioral analytics. There will be a rise in industry and sector specific AI applications where business domain knowledge and business content data are the main differentiators. However, increases in AI adoption rates do not necessarily translate into higher success rates. To avoid failure, business executives need to develop robust AI strategies and metrics, enhance data quality, and focus on AI integration and governance.

Key trends and applications for 2021 and beyond are as follows:

AI and Healthcare

Artificial intelligence played a crucial role in the detection of COVID-19. Indeed, we have seen the emergence of the use of AI at hospitals to evaluate chest CT scans. With the use of deep learning and image recognition, COVID patients could be diagnosed thus enabling the medical team to follow the necessary protocols. Another important application was the triage of COVID-19. Once a patient has been diagnosed with COVID, AI has been used to predict the likely severity of the illness so the medical staff can prioritise resources and treatments.

In a post-COVID world, we will see increased use of AI in detection of illnesses, triage of patients, and drug discovery. According to a recent market research, the market size for global healthcare IT is expected to reach $270 billion by 2020.[2] The increase will be driven by COVID-19, government policies, and the use of technologies such as artificial intelligence and big data.

AI and Supply Chains

Coronavirus has highlighted the need to re-think traditional supply chain models. There will be an increase in the use of technology such as artificial intelligence, Internet of Things, and 5G to make supply chains more efficient.

Artificial intelligence applications will focus on improving end to end visibility, analysing data to detect anomalies, and forecasting supply and demand outlooks thus making supply chains more resilient.

AI and Retail

The pandemic has changed what and how consumers buy, with retailers forced to grow their online presence. E-commerce has been put at the forefront: in the first six months of 2020 consumer spending with US retailers increased by about a third compared for the same period in 2019.[3]

According to new market research, AI in retail will be worth about $20 billion by 2027.[4] When it comes to retail and e-commerce, we can find AI applications in several areas including customers analytics for product recommendations, targeted marketing, and price optimizations.

For the latter, AI is applied to analyze patterns and data on customer profiles, their purchase power, product specification, timing of purchase, and what the competition is offering. The outcome of the analysis will set the pricing strategy. Several companies use AI to set their pricing strategy on a frequent basis, for example Amazon's average product's cost changes about every 10 minutes.[5]

AI and Intelligent Autonomous Agents

COVID has highlighted the need to deploy intelligent autonomous agents that cannot catch diseases to fight against the pandemic. We have seen both robots used at hospitals to diagnose COVID-19 patients and drones deployed to monitor if the public is adhering to social distancing rules.

An ABI research report showed that mobile robotics applications market size will increase to $23 billion by 2021.[6] This increase is mainly due to applications that disinfect, monitor, and deliver materials.

The integration of AI with drone technology and robotics will create new application opportunities and will make them mainstreamed across several sectors.

AI and Education

Education is another sector that was badly hit by COVID. According to UNICEF more than 1 billion children are at risk of falling behind due to school closures.[7] The pandemic has highlighted the need for educators to adopt digital solutions to minimise learning vulnerabilities across the globe.

AI application in education will mainly focus on personalized learning where the technology is used to design and tailor training materials that matches the student's ability and learning preferences. Other applications include the deployment of voice assistants to interact with educational material and the use of AI to support teachers in administrative tasks.

AI and Digital Twins

The pandemic has accelerated the adoption of digital twin technology. Digital twins are replicas of physical assets such as cities, offices, and factories. This technology became crucial in testing pandemic scenarios and emergency plans.

Digital twins technology is expected to reach a global spend level of about $13 billion by 2023 fueled by AI and machine learning.[8]

When integrated with artificial intelligence and IoT, digital twin technology becomes very powerful when trying to test scenarios and predict bottlenecks, breakdowns, and productivity.

AI and Ethics

Over the last year, we had several prominent examples of AI ethics issues.

The first example relates to facial recognition: after several calls against mass surveillance, racial profiling and bias, and in light of Black Lives Matter movement starting in the United States, several tech companies such as Microsoft banned the police from using its facial recognition technology.

The second example relates to the use of an algorithm to predict exam results during COVID-19 period: after accusations and protests that the controversial algorithm was biased against students from poorer backgrounds, the United Kingdom government was forced to ditch the algorithm.

In the absence of regulations and tightened frameworks, ethics will continue to be the main concerns surrounding the use of artificial intelligence. ~

ENDNOTES

1. McKinsey, Global survey of executives, October 2020. https://www.mckinsey.com/business-functions/strategy-and-corporate-finance/our-insights/how-covid-19-has-pushed-companies-over-the-technology-tipping-point-and-transformed-business-forever
2. PRnewswire, COVID-19 impact on global healthcare information technology, June 2020. https://www.prnewswire.com/news-releases/270-billion-worldwide-healthcare-information-technology-industry-to-2021---ai-and-analytics-present-lucrative-opportunities-301072916.html
3. Digitalcommerce360, how corona virus is changing e-commerce, August 2020. https://www.digitalcommerce360.com/2020/08/25/ecommerce-during-coronavirus-pandemic-in-charts/
4. PRnewswire, AI in retail market, July 2020. https://www.prnewswire.com/news-releases/artificial-intelligence-ai-in-retail-market-worth-19-9-billion-by-2027--exclusive-report-covering-pre-and-post-covid-19-market-analysis-by-meticulous-research-301098029.html
5. Business Insider, 10 August 2018. https://www.businessinsider.com/amazon-price-changes-2018-8
6. TechRepublic, Mobile robotic market, April 2020. https://www.techrepublic.com/article/mobile-robotics-market-expected-to-soar-to-23-billion-in-2021/
7. UNICEF, Education and COVID-19, September 2020. https://data.unicef.org/topic/education/covid-19/
8. Juniper Research, April 2019. https://www.juniperresearch.com/press/press-releases/digital-twin-revenues-to-reach-13-billion-2023.

Dr. Djamila Amimer founded Mind Senses Global with a mission to help businesses and organizations apply artificial intelligence.

UPSKILLING ORGANIZATIONS TO ADOPT AI

Kyle Palko

- AI Research Leader
at U.S. Air Force and MIT AI Accelerator -

Artificial intelligence (AI) has been touted as The Fourth Industrial Revolution and a technology that will transform the world, for better or for worse.[1] The technology has the opportunity to catapult developing countries past their developed peers or further centralize power in the hands of a few. Data, which fuels all machine learning (ML) and AI, is now more valuable than oil.[2] In fact, data science and artificial intelligence are sometimes referred to as the sexiest jobs in the 21st Century.[3]

While there are many hypotheses about how the future of AI shapes the world, one idea remains consistent: Artificial intelligence will only be a transformative technology if organizations are ready to use it.

There are technical requirements that can be solved through means such as data, IT infrastructure, and software development, but talent management — the people problem — is likely to prove more challenging.

According to LinkedIn, AI related job descriptions such as "AI Engineers" or "ML Researchers" have seen 74% annual growth from 2016-2019. Data science is close behind, with 37% annual growth.[4] Unfortunately, the number of job listings is quickly outpacing the supply of AI practitioners. In a recent survey on AI adoption, Deloitte found that 68% of business leaders reported a moderate-to-extreme AI skills gap in their workforce.[5] Additionally, Tencent estimated that while there are over a million AI roles available, there are only 300,000 AI practitioners in the world.[6] Worse yet, there are only an estimated 22,000 PhD-educated AI experts deemed qualified to lead research and novel application development.[7]

In order to overcome this hurdle, organizations must prepare to revitalize their workforce. Not every person on an AI engineering team needs to be an expert, but they should have a fundamental understanding of the technology. Teams building artificial intelligence applications also need domain expertise to be successful. Applications are more likely to flourish if the domain experts are knowledgeable in AI because understanding the requirements for training, testing, and deploying models can streamline processes and lead to quicker adoption. Ultimately, this means that most organizations may only require a core group of AI practioners supported by teams who understand the basics of AI.

However, organizations that wish to adopt AI as a meaningful technology will have difficulties hiring the qualified teams they desire.

Bridging the AI skills gap through hiring is competitive and requires sufficient time for the new hires to learn the business processes. As a reflection of the current market state, compensation packages for AI engineering positions regularly exceed $200,000 as companies seek to attract the most qualified candidates.[8] Moreover, given the widening gap between the supply and demand of AI talent, organizations are increasingly looking internally to fill their ranks.

Although increasing numbers of individuals with AI schooling are entering the job market, organizations investing in their own workforce will reap the benefits of capitalizing on a readily available talent pool. Individuals within an organization are already familiar with the organization's processes and products, making them viable candidates for AI talent development. Such employees are better positioned to provide insights not readily apparent to new hires. With additional training and education, these individuals can attain advanced technical skills required to employ artificial intelligence. We call this process of providing new skills to individuals "upskilling."[9]

It is important to note that upskilling does not always require formal education. The market for this type of learning is already well established and expanding.

In-person coding bootcamps, often conducted full time for several weeks, were estimated to graduate 23,000 students in 2019, where it was reported that most had never had any programming background.[10] Online bootcamps were also starting to gain traction before the COVID-19 pandemic and graduated 5,919 students in 2019.[11] Quality of bootcamp training is high, as demonstrated by the reported 90% job placement rate of many offerings.[12]

While full time, short-term learning has proven extremely successful, a greater majority of individuals in organizations are more likely to benefit from just-in-time learning. Research suggests that people can effectively learn and retain knowledge during random opportunities—whether on a coffee break, a commute to work, or before bed.[13] This means that organizations can use online training offerings through higher education, massively open online courses (MOOCs) such as edX, Coursera, and Udemy, and even from individual contributors around the globe. These platforms provide individuals the opportunity to learn on their own time, at their own pace.

Although the pandemic has demonstrated both positives and negatives of online learning, case studies have shown that every dollar invested in online training results in $30 in productivity gains.[14] However, corporate employers and other organizations must also provide opportunities to convert students' personal learning investments into credentials that are valued by the organization, otherwise the completion rate will suffer, or worse, those individuals will leave with the new skills they gained.

Leading technology companies have already recognized the need for a more technologically skilled workforce to adopt AI. Amazon, AT&T, and Mastercard are investing over $2.2 billion to upskill over 250,000 of their employees in the digital age.[15,16,17] Call centers in the Philippines view AI as an opportunity to embrace by upskilling rather than lament about jobs lost to automation.[18]

Even the U.S. military is investing in upskilling as the world turns increasingly digital. Often seen as the most technologically advanced branch of the military, the U.S. Air Force recently announced initiatives aimed at curating a more digital workforce through training incentives and learning opportunities for its Airmen.[19] The U.S. Space Force employed similar programming not long after.[20]

The reality is, artificial intelligence technology is here. Organizations that are most likely to effectively use it are those that have a digitally competent workforce. Upskilling an organization's workforce presents a strategy to more effectively mitigate the skills gap. The COVID-19 pandemic and the increasing prevalence of working from home present new opportunities to launch technical training initiatives to upskill the workforce. Many organizations across the globe are already making these investments and more are sure to follow suit. ~

Disclaimer: The views expressed in this essay are those of the author and do not reflect the official policy or position of the U.S. Air Force, Department of Defense, or the U.S. Government.

ENDNOTES

1. https://en.unesco.org/courier/2018-3/fourth-revolution
2. https://www.economist.com/leaders/2017/05/06/the-worlds-most-valuable-resource-is-no-longer-oil-but-data
3. https://hbr.org/2012/10/data-scientist-the-sexiest-job-of-the-21st-century
4. https://business.linkedin.com/content/dam/me/business/en-us/talent-solutions/emerging-jobs-report/Emerging_Jobs_Report_U.S._FINAL.pdf
5. https://www2.deloitte.com/us/en/insights/focus/cognitive-technologies/ai-adoption-in-the-workforce.html
6. https://www.theverge.com/2017/12/5/16737224/global-ai-talent-shortfall-tencent-report
7. https://jfgagne.ai/talent/
8. https://www.talentseer.com/2020-ai-talent-report
9. https://www.merriam-webster.com/dictionary/upskill
10. https://www.coursereport.com/coding-bootcamp-ultimate-guide
11. Ibid.
12. https://careerkarma.com/blog/coding-bootcamp-job-placement/
13. https://dl.acm.org/doi/abs/10.1145/205323.205345
14. https://www.ibm.com/services/learning/pdfs/IBMTraining-TheValueofTraining.pdf
15. https://www.aboutamazon.com/working-at-amazon/upskilling-2025
16. https://www.cnbc.com/2018/03/13/atts-1-billion-gambit-retraining-nearly-half-its-workforce.html
17. https://www.humanresourcesonline.net/upskilling-101-how-mastercard-has-developed-and-scaled-fit-for-purpose-learning-experiences
18. https://www.scmp.com/week-asia/economics/article/3073999/artificial-intelligence-friend-or-foe-philippine-call-centre
19. https://www.fedscoop.com/air-forces-digital-university-free-technical-training/
20. https://www.fedscoop.com/space-force-workforce-personnel-digital-fluency/

Kyle Palko is a Captain in the U.S. Air Force and leads AI research teams at the Air Force/MIT AI Accelerator.

Photo by Nick Morrison on Unsplash.

THE FUTURE OF ROBOTS: HUMAN-ROBOT INTERACTION AND ARTIFICIAL INTELLIGENCE

Ragu Athinarayanan, Michael Walton,
Xiumin Diao, Balamurugan Balakreshnan

- Purdue University and Microsoft Corporation -

Current Status of Robots

Although robots have been in development for more than half a century, their applications are still limited to a few select industries such as automotive and electronics. The majority of these robots are conventional industrial robots that work in manufacturing facilities with the presence of safety equipment such as fences and cages.

Conventional industrial robots are basically pre-programed machines that are adept at automating non-variable production lines. Their typical tasks include welding, painting, assembly, pick -and-place, material handling, etc. Conventional industrial robots usually cannot work interactively with humans due to safety concerns.

A collaborative robot is a relatively new type of industrial robot that intends to physically interact with humans directly and safely in a shared workspace. Thanks to technologies such as artificial intelligence (AI) and their onboard safety mechanisms, collaborative robots do not need safety fences or cages for safe operation.

Collaborative robots make it possible to take full advantage of the strength and speed of robots and the creativity and ingenuity of humans. While collaborative robots are still a nascent market compared to conventional industrial robots, they have experienced rapid market growth in the past decade and are expected to continue to expand their market share quickly in the future.

Due to rapid technological advancements, robots are reaching new industries and applications. There is a huge demand for service robots in the consumer and service fields, such as medical care, elder care, health, rehabilitation, and education. A service robot is intended to assist humans or perform tasks on their behalf, rather than to replace humans. Compared to conventional industrial robots, service robots usually work in unstructured environments and collaborate directly with humans. Service robots have become more popular in recent years.

Robots have to be truly intelligent to be integrated into the workplace, so they are situationally aware of potential interactions with humans.

For this reason, human-robot interaction (HRI) and AI are the core technologies that will enable future robotics in the workplace.

Automation Challenges and Human-Robot Collaboration

The old adage with Industry 3.0 is that maximizing automation also increases productivity. With the advent of Industry 4.0 and the emergence of technologies such as AI in the workplace, this may not be true anymore. The maturity of AI-enabled HRI will cause factories to start moving away from maximizing automation to improve productivity.

Mercedes-Benz is doing just that, moving away from trying to maximize automation, with humans playing a bigger role in industrial production. BMW is on the same trajectory, having determined that AI-enabled HRI in their automotive factories is 85% more productive than either humans or robots working on their own. Hence, for future factories, the question is not how much workforce AI will replace; rather, it is how will AI empower the workforce and allow humans to work alongside robots in factories?

COVID-19 has also highlighted the need to create more resilient supply chains and the importance of human workers in manufacturing. One example of this occurred when automakers were called on to re-purpose their factories for emergency production of medical equipment in the pandemic. The retooling became a lengthy and onerous process due to excessive and rigid automation processes that were already in place.

Highly automated factories that did not have the flexibility for a rapid change struggled to meet these demands, because it can take weeks or months to reprogram and refit automated production lines. Additionally, when factoring in costly downtime, most were unable to respond to this request for emergency production during the pandemic.

The adaptability of human workers paired with robots that are collaborative only requires a day or perhaps a few days for some reprogramming. The flexibility of human-robot collaboration in these situations would allow for manufacturers to easily adapt to the shifting demand with new products and processes, not to mention the production efficiency gained from combining the strength and speed of robots with the creativity and ingenuity of humans. In short, factories become more flexible and agile, and manufacturers can respond in a rapid fashion to situations such as the pandemic or when the digital supply networks are disrupted.

Collaborative robots integrate the cognitive capabilities and quick adaptation skills of humans, while maintaining the speed, strength, and repeatability of conventional robots.

As collaborative robots become mainstream across industries, it will become increasingly evident that the skills expected from collaborative robots are significantly different from what is expected from conventional industrial robots. The need to work closely with humans to perform challenging tasks requires that collaborative robots interact with humans efficiently and effectively.

For example, understanding human intention during a collaborative task and adjusting the interaction controller of the robot accordingly to comply with human intention has been a major challenge in human-robot interactions until the recent emergence of artificial intelligence in robotics.

Artificial Intelligence in Robotics

The majority of robots today lack cognitive skills and cannot solve simple problems that are considered trivial for humans. For example, conventional industrial robots cannot pick up a part on an assembly line, even if the part is displaced by only a few inches.

AI-based computation models and architectures, when integrated into robots, allow them to acquire cognitive skills and enable them to emulate human cognition with a certain level of intelligence. With collaborative robots, making them intelligent is not only critical, but also a prerequisite before they can be deployed to perform tasks requiring interactions with humans.

Artificial intelligence that integrates computer science, mathematics, cognitive science, neurology, and social science has become one of the core driving forces behind AI-enabled HRI and the new industrial transformation. For this reason, many countries are making significant investments in artificial intelligence. The European Commission alone invested $24 billion in artificial intelligence from 2018 to 2020. France announced the "French Artificial Intelligence Strategy" in May 2018.

In June 2018, Japan proposed the "Future Investment Strategy 2018" focused on promoting the construction of the Internet of Things and the application of artificial intelligence. In July 2017, China released the "New Generation Artificial Intelligence Development Plan" and identified the following five strategic artificial intelligence areas: big data intelligence, group intelligence, cross-media intelligence, human-machine hybrid enhancement intelligence, and autonomous intelligent systems.

Artificial intelligence can be classified into two categories: artificial narrow intelligence (ANI) and artificial general intelligence (AGI). ANI deals with artificial intelligence for a specific purpose while AGI is for a general purpose. The development of ANI has been impressive with many important breakthroughs in the past decade.

The requirements and the boundary of the specific task is usually clear, and the artificial intelligence model is relatively simple to develop. Thus, an ANI system is relatively easy to create. The recent progress of artificial intelligence is mainly concentrated in ANI.

The human brain can be compared to an AGI system that solves problems by drawing inferences from various inputs such as vision, hearing, judgment, reasoning, learning, thinking, planning, and design. How to develop an AGI system is one of the goals in the development of the next generation of artificial intelligence.

In October 2016, the National Science and Technology Commission of the United States issued the National Artificial Intelligence Research and Development Strategic Plan, proposing to focus on AGI in the long-term development strategy of artificial intelligence in the United States. The co-founder of DeepMind, Demis Hassabis, proposed to create an AGI system that can solve all problems in the world. Microsoft established an AGI Laboratory in 2017, with many scientists involved in perception, learning, reasoning, and natural language understanding.

Based on developments particularly in ANI, artificial intelligence has made significant progress in information perception and machine learning to advance human-robot collaboration in the workplace. We think that with human capital remaining extremely important, it is clear that robots working collaboratively with humans is the way of the near future. AI-enabled HRI that is integrated with human capital will be key to making this work. The ROI is simply too great to ignore.

We predict that over the next 10 years, many companies will continue to increase spend globally on collaborative robots (leveraging AI), particularly in the manufacturing and retail industries. ~

About the Authors: Through a joint partnership between Purdue University and Microsoft Corporation, the authors are working on developing an Intelligent Manufacturing curriculum for the future workforce.

THE NEW, NEW NORMAL

Jason Schenker

- Chairman of The Futurist Institute-

Following the outbreak of COVID-19, countless industries were disrupted. Many began referring to the dynamics impacting e-commerce, remote work, tourism, and other industries as the *new normal.*

With COVID vaccine distribution ahead, questions about the future are significant. Some wonder if the new normal will stick. Others question if we will wind the clock back and go back to the *old normal.*

In true Hegelian fashion, I expect that the technological *Weltgeist* will propel us forward into a synthesis of both the old normal and the new normal. It will be a *new, new normal.* Some industries that have experienced growth during the pandemic could remain strong or accelerate further, while those that have been weak are likely to lurch forward into recovery.

Manufacturing Strength

One of the areas of greatest strength in the wake of the COVID-19 pandemic has been manufacturing. While services demand has remained significantly depressed, and real GDP is likely to take quarters to return to pre-pandemic levels, there was a relatively short contraction in U.S., Eurozone, and Chinese manufacturing reflected in the purchasing manager indices (PMIs) as seen in Figure A.

This contraction was especially short-lived when compared to the contractions during the Great Recession from 2007 to 2009. This dynamic can be seen in the aggregated sum of the U.S. ISM, Eurozone PMI, and Chinese Caixin PMI in Figure B.

Figure A: Global PMIs[1]

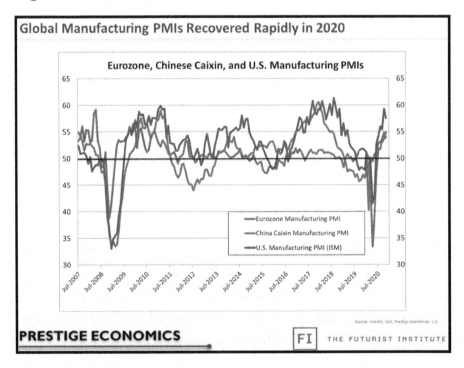

Part of the reason that U.S. and global manufacturing have recovered rapidly and forcefully is because of low interest rates. After all, manufacturing is a tremendously interest rate sensitive industry, and central banks moved rapidly to lower interest rates as the Fed quickly bought up investment grade — and some high yield — corporate debt by expanding its balance sheet.

Looking to 2021 and beyond, interest rates are likely to remain exceptionally low. In fact, forecasts from members of the U.S. Federal Reserve Open Market Committee in September 2020 reflect that the Fed is likely to keep rates near zero into at least 2024. This dynamic is likely to be true globally.

Figure B: Sum of Global PMIs[2]

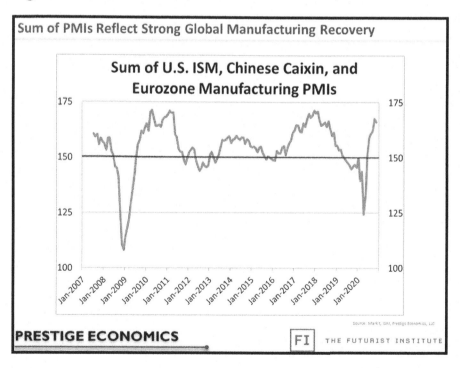

As we look ahead to 2021, the Fed is also likely to continue buying up mortgages and treasuries. This dynamic, combined with low interest rates globally, is likely to remain generally supportive of manufacturing — and it is likely to be supportive for industrial metals demand and prices.

One area of manufacturing that is likely to remain particularly strong is material handling equipment manufacturing. This critical sector has been supported by a surge in e-commerce as a result of COVID-19. Although e-commerce has been rising on trend for years, e-commerce as a percent of retail sales rose to a record 16.1 percent in the second quarter of 2020. The rise from 11.8 percent in the first quarter of 2020 can be seen in Figure C.

Figure C: E-Commerce Percent of Retail[3]

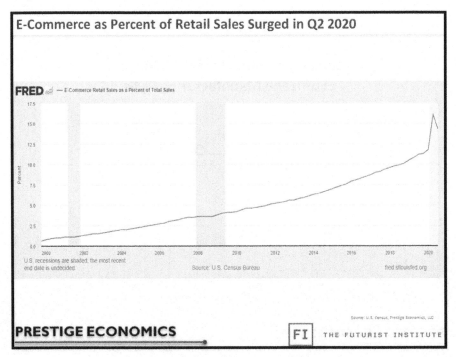

The percentage fell in the third quarter of 2020, when e-commerce as a percent of retail fell to 14.3 percent. Despite this pullback, it did not represent a full drop to the 11.8 percent of e-commerce retail seen in the first quarter. Looking ahead to 2021, it seems likely e-commerce retail percentages could remain above the percentages seen prior to COVID-19.

Beyond supportive e-commerce dynamics, material handling overall stands to be strong in 2021. This is something reflected in Figure D, which shows the percent of material handling industry leaders who expect new orders twelve months in the future to be higher than in the present. This series hit a record level of 100 percent in three different months of 2020 through November.

Figure D: Future New Orders for Material Handling[4]

In other words, there were several months in 2020 when 100 percent of material handling industry leaders expected 2021 new orders to be higher than in 2020.

Lurching Toward Recovery

While manufacturing and material handling industries are poised to remain strong in the new, new normal, other industries and sectors could still struggle to recover. Service industries, in particular, are likely to struggle in the year ahead. One area of weakness that is likely to improve significantly in 2021 as we move to the new, new normal is travel and tourism. But this sector has a long way to go, and vaccinations will not be an overnight panacea.

Figure E: TSA Throughput[5]

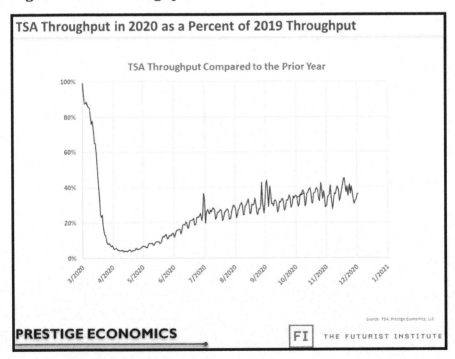

U.S. Transportation Security Administration (TSA) year-on-year throughput has been the best proxy to understand how much travel has taken a hit in 2020. Although down by over 90 percent in April 2020, TSA throughput was still down 67 percent in 2020, compared to November 2019 levels. This dynamic can be seen in Figure E. In 2021, the figure to watch for improvements will be TSA throughput in 2021 compared to 2019 levels.

Tourism and travel could still remain depressed in 2021, as corporate travel and entertainment expenses remain tight, and retail consumers remain both skittish of travel because of the pandemic as well as cost conscious, due to the negative economic impacts of COVID-19.

Along those lines, it is important to recognize that there are a lot of unemployed Americans in 2020, compared to 2019. To see just how many, look at the weekly jobless claims report compiled by the U.S. Department of Labor. While most people focus on initial claims and continuing claims, the best point of reference for COVID-19 dynamics is the table with the persons claiming unemployment insurance benefits in all programs (unadjusted), which is shown in Figure F.

For the week ending 14 November 2020, there were almost 20.2 million Americans collecting unemployment insurance across all categories. The prior year, there were less than 1.6 million. That is a massive difference, and while 2021 is likely to be a year of improvements, the job market is likely to be slow to recover, regardless of how quickly vaccines can be distributed. After all, the labor market is notoriously sticky in economic recovery.

Figure F: U.S. Joblessness in November 2020[6]

Over 20 Million Collecting Unemployment in November 2020

PERSONS CLAIMING UI BENEFITS IN ALL PROGRAMS (UNADJUSTED)

WEEK ENDING	November 14	November 7	Change	Prior Year[1]
Regular State	5,890,222	6,037,760	-147,538	1,541,892
Federal Employees	14,494	13,539	+955	8,561
Newly Discharged Veterans	11,154	11,201	-47	5,752
Pandemic Unemployment Assistance[3]	8,869,502	9,208,570	-339,068	NA
Pandemic Emergency UC[4]	4,569,016	4,509,284	+59,732	NA
Extended Benefits[5]	681,075	601,377	+79,698	0
State Additional Benefits[6]	2,625	2,560	+65	5,811
STC / Workshare[7]	125,389	128,819	-3,430	11,469
TOTAL[8]	20,163,477	20,513,110	-349,633	1,573,485

Source: DOL, Prestige Economics, LLC

PRESTIGE ECONOMICS   FI   THE FUTURIST INSTITUTE

Weakness in the labor market could limit some economic upside potential in 2021 — especially for service businesses. But overall GDP growth, manufacturing, and material handling are still poised for solid growth in the year ahead. ~

ENDNOTES

1. PMI data retrieved from the Institute of Supply Management, IHS Markit, TradingEconomics.com, and Econoday.com.
2. Ibid.
3. U.S. Census Bureau, E-Commerce Retail Sales as a Percent of Total Sales [ECOMPCTSA], retrieved from FRED, Federal Reserve Bank of St. Louis; https://fred.stlouisfed.org/series/ECOMPCTSA, 7 December 2020.
4. MHI BAI by Prestige Economics, November 2020.
5. https://www.tsa.gov/coronavirus/passenger-throughput
6. https://www.dol.gov/ui/data.pdf. Retrieved on 7 December 2020.

Jason Schenker is the Chairman of The Futurist Institute.

AUTOMATION WILL OVERCOME SUPPLY CHAIN WEAKNESSES EXPOSED BY COVID-19

Matthew Frazier

- Engineering Manager at Murata Machinery USA -

Any reflection on the year 2020 would be incomplete without considering the impact of the COVID-19 pandemic. In manufacturing and logistics, global shutdowns caused supply chain interruptions, production slowdowns, and missed fulfillment deadlines prompting widespread shortages of essential products.

From many perspectives, these shortages and interruptions are cause for concern.

The good news is that the supply chain weaknesses exposed by COVID-19 are nothing new; the pandemic has simply intensified the urgency to address them. And widely available automated solutions can already solve a good proportion of these problems.

THE ROBOT AND AUTOMATION ALMANAC - 2021   81

These realities make the economic case for automation greater than ever, and point to shifting perceptions toward automation, readiness to embrace it, and a future where manual and machine labor is increasingly blended.

Muratec's Uni-SHUTTLE HP fulfillment technology.

Challenge #1: Labor Shortages and Worker Safety

Labor shortages and worker safety concerns are closely related: it's harder to attract and retain skilled workers in dangerous or uncomfortable working environments. The skilled labor shortage has been affecting manufacturing and logistics for years. The pandemic intensified this trend, contributing to workforce absences and adding the threat of contagion to safety concerns.

Automation is ideal for performing two broad classes of tasks: 1) the mundane, repetitive, and easily predictable, and 2) high-precision tasks beyond the capabilities of human skill. In both scenarios, automated systems lessen the burden on individual workers, enhance their productivity, and minimize accidents and injuries.

For instance, the top five types of workplace injuries are caused by contact with harmful objects (40%), overexertion (24%), slips and falls (19%), repetitive motion (8%), and contact with hazardous substances or chemicals (6%).[1] Material handling solutions such as automated guided vehicles (AGVs), automated storage and retrieval systems (AS/RS), and goods-to-person solutions readily address these hazards by reducing physical labor, limiting work in hazardous environments, and by transporting dangerous substances.

Few workplace accidents have been attributed to these types of solutions, and today's smart AGVs come equipped with redundant safety features to make them capable of responding and reacting to the surrounding environment.

In one recent cross-industry survey of CFOs, 78% said they plan to reconfigure worksites to promote physical distancing, 53% will change shifts and/or alternate crews to reduce exposure, and 44% will specifically prioritize automation as a new way of working.[2] In manufacturing and logistics, automated systems are key to accomplishing the first two goals, as machines can reduce human contact and enable 24/7 production while minimizing operational costs.

A popular but flawed criticism of automation is that it replaces human workers, robbing them of their livelihoods. The COVID-19 pandemic could help shift this negative perception by underscoring the positive impact of automation on worker safety. Automation doesn't replace workers; it supplements and protects them. When repetitive or dangerous tasks are automated, companies can shift employees to other areas and increase cross-training, helping people to perform valuable roles in more comfortable working environments.

Challenge #2: E-commerce Fulfillment Pressure
Brick-and-mortar shopping has been losing ground to e-commerce for decades, but 2020 compounded that trend into a necessity. Reliance on online ordering pressures warehouses and fulfillment centers to increase SKUs and fulfill orders at lightning speed to stay competitive. It has also highlighted needs and opportunities within the cold supply chain, with food and groceries as the second-fastest growing category in e-commerce.[3]

The repetitive, predictable nature of warehouse and fulfillment operations makes them an ideal candidate for increased automation.

Warehouse automation is the second largest investment area for logistics companies, just behind cloud logistics, which could be viewed as related technology since cloud solutions underpin massive automation endeavors.[4] In fact, 99% of cold chain businesses say their planned automation investments, which were already significant before the pandemic, will remain the same or increase in light of new demand.[5]

The benefits of automation in the fulfillment sector are clear and widely accepted. Best-in-class automated distribution centers achieve 95% on-time deliveries, one and a half times more often than the national average.[6] They also realize up to 85% in space savings, thanks to the small footprints and compact integration of various automation technologies.

Challenge #3: Driving Production Home
Historically, many industries have concentrated production operations in countries with the lowest manufacturing costs, with China topping the list.[7]

In recent years, experts in the U.S. and Europe have called for increased domestic production. While some of this desire is rooted in dissatisfaction over quality or delivery time, there are also environmental, political, and socioeconomic arguments that have deepened since the onset of the pandemic.

Environmentalists have criticized Chinese producers for pollution and waste, with some experts attesting that more rigorous Chinese anti-pollution laws passed in 2016 are insufficient to address the scope and scale of the problem.[8] Additionally, overseas production inherently contributes to carbon emissions because of its reliance on long-distance transportation. Since some experts believe that habitat destruction and climate change contribute to pandemics, environmental concerns are heightened.[9]

From a political and economic perspective, supply chain interruptions highlighted a need for domestic manufacturing, especially for products deemed essential. A prime example is the U.S. government's efforts to rebuild the country's pharmaceutical manufacturing industry, with billions of dollars in public and private funds already committed.[10]

Confronting environmental challenges requires domestic production and energy-efficient facilities. The biggest barrier to domestic production is cost. How can onshore manufacturing operations compete with overseas prices with minimal environmental impact? Once again, automation holds the answer.

While robots and automated machinery do perform energy-intensive processes, many of today's machines are designed to consume as little electricity as possible.

Prior to the pandemic, increased energy efficiency was considered a major contributing factor in the growth of the industrial automation market.[11]

The green potential of industrial automation lies in the connected and programmable nature of these automated processes, which grants precision control over when and how these systems consume power, especially when integrated into larger energy management strategies.

Synergistically, consuming less power also keeps overall production costs down. Increased automation is associated with up to 65% decrease in operational costs[12] thanks to energy efficiency, process efficiency, higher throughput, and less reliance on manual intervention — all without sacrificing quality. Furthermore, automation enables 24/7 production, further driving cost competitiveness and business value.

Muratec forklift AGV displaying warehouse capabilities.

Demand for Automation and Advances in Technology

While we may have yet to see the full impact of COVID-19, the economic case for automation is greater than ever. Many businesses will increasingly blend cost-effective automation technology into manual operations to stay competitive.

Investors and stakeholders may wonder if standard industrial automation solutions like guided carts or AGVs will be quickly phased out by more advanced, free-moving, artificially intelligent robots. While advanced robotics hold promise and may one day become the industry norm, and advances are constantly being made, the classic question of cost and scale will likely keep much of today's automated technology in play for a long time.

While enterprises like Amazon are known for warehouse and distribution innovation, small-to-medium size operations are as likely to see ROI on today's core automated technologies, saving on operational costs, repurposing labor for value-driven tasks, and increasing productivity. For many facilities, 2020 has been the tipping point for turning these solutions into business necessities. ~

ENDNOTES

1. https://www.assemblymag.com/ext/resources/White_Papers/2019/sep/UR_Workplace-Injuries-White-Paper-Final_May2019.pdf
2. https://www.pwc.com/us/en/library/covid-19/pwc-covid-19-cfo-pulse-survey.html
3. https://www.semrush.com/blog/2020-digital-marketing-trends-in-ecommerce/
4. https://www.statista.com/statistics/780763/inventory-management-investments-retailers-manufacturers/
5. https://www.gcca.org/sites/default/files/ImpactsCOVID-19onColdChain-May%202020-final.pdf
6. https://www.roboticsbusinessreview.com/supply-chain/full-warehouse-automation-is-the-goal-and-the-opportunity-for-both-provider
7. https://www.usnews.com/news/best-countries/slideshows/countries-seen-to-have-the-lowest-manufacturing-costs
8. https://scholar.harvard.edu/files/jaldy/files/the_debate_forum_2018_sept-oct.pdf
9. https://www.medpagetoday.com/infectiousdisease/covid19/86325
10. https://www.bmj.com/content/370/bmj.m3393
11. https://www.vdcresearch.com/News-events/ias-blog/Five-Industrial-Automation-Trends-in-2017.html
12. https://www.thelogisticsiq.com/research/warehouse-automation-market/

Matthew Frazier is Murata Machinery, USA's Logistics and Automation Engineering Manager, bringing more than 15 years of experience in engineering and product design.

...BUT IS IT SAFE?

Patrick Davison

- Director of Standards at MHI -

Technological advancements are outpacing our ability to assess their attributes. Are they effective? Are they safe? The short answer: "Maybe...it depends."

We are living in a time where rapid technological innovations in robotics and automation technologies have capabilities that were unthinkable just a few years ago. E-commerce is both a catalyst and a beneficiary of these advancements.

Technological advancements in supply chain applications are improving order fulfillment efficiency, which in turn is fueling innovation into developing new products and solutions to fulfill the demand for continued improvements in selection, convenience, and delivery.

MODEX 2020 attendees observing material handling robots.
Image provided by MHI.

Sensors and processing are constantly improving, making them ubiquitous, reliable, and inexpensive, which in turn means they are appearing in more and more devices. For material handling automation technologies, they can help to identify the objects they are designed to engage with (such as docking stations or boxes of inventory) while avoiding stationary obstacles (such as building columns or storage racks) and moving objects (such as vehicles and personnel) in their environment.

But are there unanticipated consequences associated with the deployment of these technologies?

The question pertaining to the safe deployment of new technologies can be a tricky one to answer. Our legal and regulatory environment is not progressing at the same rate as the automation solutions they are asked to address.

Traditionally, we rely on standards in cases where there are no specific regulations pertaining to a particular technology area (and most newer technologies have no such regulations that apply to them). In effect, we can claim compliance with industry standards as a determination of the safety of a product, technology, or system.

However, standards typically lag technology since it is difficult, if not impossible, to write a standard for a technology that is not fully realized. Development of a new standard can take years to complete, and that activity typically does not begin in earnest until the technology achieves commercialization.

Standards are the egg that comes after the chicken. Additionally, attributes such as effectiveness and safety often depend on how a technology is integrated or deployed.

A case in point is autonomous mobile robots (AMRs). AMRs are capable of performing tasks associated with goods picking and movement that would otherwise need to be performed by employees, and typically provide the enterprise that deploys them a rapid return on investment.

AMRs are being deployed in warehouse and distribution centers to perform a variety of tasks associated with the movement of goods in those facilities.

They are equipped with on-board sensors and processors to make sense of their environment so they can perform tasks while avoiding potentially hazardous contact with property and personnel.

The AMR market was in its infancy when Amazon bought Kiva, an industry pioneer, in 2012. Fast forward to 2020, where there were nearly 20 companies exhibiting AMRs at MODEX 2020. The value proposition of AMRs has expanded a market that did not exist a decade ago.

Concurrent with the growth of the AMR market has been an effort to develop American National Standards covering AMR test methods and safety attributes. ASTM formed the F45 Committee for Driverless Automatic Guided Industrial Vehicles in 2014, and the Robotic Industries Association began the creation of an AMR safety standard in 2015.

To date, ASTM has published six standards covering topics ranging from docking and navigation to communication and integration, and RIA is on the verge of publishing the first part of the AMR safety standard applicable to manufacturers in late 2020. Meanwhile, manufacturers, regulators, and users of AMRs have created and deployed AMRs with incomplete coverage of safety standards for a decade.

The absence of a safety standard for a product category does not imply that a technology is or is not safe. Rather, the determination of safety requirements is conducted on a case-by-case basis since consensus in the form of a standard on what constitutes a safe deployment has not been determined.

But all hope is not lost!

We can utilize "Type B" standards, such as ANSI B11.0 and B11.19 to assess risks and safeguards, respectively, associated with a particular application. This process relies on identifying all anticipated tasks (including deployment, operation, maintenance, and decommissioning) and associated hazards associated with the operations utilizing the technology. After this list is created, the implementation of devices (such as machine guards, safety sensors, or PPE) and processes (such as personnel training and safe work practices) to reduce risk to an acceptable level is proposed and enacted.

Technologies utilizing safety sensors can be evaluated to the requirements of ISO 13849-1 to assure that sensor and processor circuitry is sufficiently robust to identify and react to hazardous conditions.

Safety professionals must also realize a product designed and built in accordance with applicable industry standards can be deployed to perform "unsafe" tasks, which emphasizes the importance of a task-based risk assessment at the deployment level.

This issue will continue to expand as we continue to deploy new technology.

Open source, artificial intelligence, virtual reality, blockchain, cloud computing, and Internet of Things are just examples of the technological or process advancements that could be incorporated into automation solutions, and they could have potential safety implications that have not been fully explored.

Once again, it is important to emphasize that these technologies are implanted with "ticking time bombs"; rather, it is likely that despite best intentions from all parties involved, our existing infrastructure for evaluating equipment safety will continue to lag behind the deployment of new technologies. Early adopters are encouraged to perform due diligence but will still likely serve as test subjects as technologies are fully deployed in the economy.

A final concern lies with the standards committees themselves. Standards committees are prone to "brain drain" associated with retirement of the aging workforce, employee turnover, and modern, lean companies seem increasingly reluctant to volunteer the expertise of their staff to the development of standards, citing a lack of a short-term ROI associated with their brightest employees volunteering their time working on standards projects rather than revenue-generating projects.

The lagging of standards behind technological innovations can introduce hazards and increase liability as new, unvetted technologies are introduced to operations.

The standards development model as a means of liability mitigation has proven to be effective, but it relies on experts to volunteer their expertise to a standards development activity which can be time-consuming and arduous. ~

Patrick Davison is the Managing Executive of The Robotics Group and Director of Standards at MHI, where he is responsible for administering the development of over 30 American National Standards for material handling technologies and administers U.S. Technical Advisory Groups for several ISO standards committees.

DISRUPT AUTOMATION WITH USER EXPERIENCE DESIGN

Cecilia Boström

- User Experience Lead at Kollmorgen -

Companies working toward the consumer market have long invested in and understood the value of user experience (UX) design. A good user experience is a key differentiator in today's market, and by aligning your company to ensure that your customers get the best possible experience at every touchpoint, you are building your brand and your customer relations over the long term.

This is true whether you are delivering goods or services to end-customers or solely engage in B2B. However, the B2B industry sector does not seem to act upon the same sense of urgency of delivering excellent user experiences as the B2C-sector. It is in most cases a lot easier for unhappy end-customers to swap their goods or services for the offering of the competitor than for business customers to do the same.

The competition is there, nonetheless. Just because a particular business segment has not been challenged yet does not mean it will not be.

Customers' demands and expectations are ever changing, and what was once considered desirable might not necessarily be so in the future. Consider customer expectations for cars, for example. When Tesla appeared from the side, selling luxury electric cars and winning significant market share, older car brands such as Volvo rushed to invest in electrifying their car fleet. Suddenly, electrification was an important differentiator. Thus, Tesla changed the rules of the game and disrupted the entire automotive industry.

Practicing UX design forces you to work from an outside-in perspective, starting with your target users, and working your way in. The essence of UX is to identify and fulfill user needs, not simply delivering on what users say that they want. A famous saying attributed to Henry Ford goes as follows: "If I had asked people what they wanted, they would have said faster horses." It is also a quote that often appears within the UX community to highlight the importance of finding the root cause of a user problem.

Nevertheless, many companies dream up features inside the comfort of the office without any real understanding of the users they are targeting — sometimes even without a clear objective on what problem to solve.

When engaging in UX, you must be able to answer the following questions:

- What are we trying to achieve?
- For whom?
- And why?

Being able to answer these three questions, will help you stay focused on the business outcomes and not get stuck into the details of the potential solution.

This will also keep your mind open to new ideas and opportunities on how to deliver on the user's needs. And above all, by being able to answer why, you make sure that you are aligned with your company's value framework and your own ethical standpoint.

Sometimes, killing a darling in its early phase is the best thing you can do for your business.

Usability as a Means for Faster Growth
Usability is a major part of user experience design and providing your users with tools that are easy to use will inevitably save them time and effort. Given that automating a business still requires a lot of manual work, we need to fine tune the tools needed to install an automated system.

Enhanced usability pays off in the long run.

For instance, imagine a task taking five minutes to perform. Now imagine how many times this task must be performed. Let us say twice a day. Then multiply that by the number of people having to perform it. Let us say we have two people working with this task. Now, adding the numbers together, over the course of a year with 260 working days, this five-minute task takes in total around 87 hours per year. Or put in other words, roughly over two full working weeks.

So seemingly small things can be worth looking into and improve on, as they may have big financial impacts over time.

To enable a continued fast growth of automation, we need to consider making all the activities around the installation process significantly easier to use. We can no longer require people to have an engineering background to be able to install an automated system.

This means that the tools that were once designed by engineers for other engineers need to drastically decrease in complexity. Fast growth requires ease of use. To achieve this, we need to understand and empathize with our target users and continuously test that we are on the right track.

Understand User Needs Before Investing in Tech Trends
It is easy to get seduced by emerging technological trends and feel the urgency to invest in whatever seems to be the hottest thing at the moment.

Be it machine learning, digital twins, blockchain technology, or 5G, we need to trust the UX process and ensure the focus lies on how we can make business while serving our users' needs.

Surely, AI might be an excellent enabler to solve a specific problem. But merely kicking off an AI initiative without a clear outcome in mind is a big risk and may just end up costing our business a lot of unnecessary effort.

Usability tests will be increasingly important.

There are loads of examples of innovative technology initiatives that failed to meet any user need and thus ended up as failures. However, when starting every initiative from our customers' perspective, we are forcing ourselves to be considerate about what technology we are using to solve a particular problem. We will also have to consider whether the problem is actually worth solving.

When we put our customers and their experiences at the top of the agenda, we must stop assuming things and instead head out and meet them.

We need to talk to our users and watch them interact with our products and services, take notice of their behavior and study their context.

By doing this, we gradually start to understand their reality and over time we will build up user empathy. Being able to empathize with our users is a superpower that will lead to more mindful problem solving.

For example, the solutions might look quite different when we are designing tools for application engineers working in calm office environments and for service technicians working in noisy production facilities. Hence, applying UX practices when jumping on the wave of the Fourth Industrial Revolution ensures that we stay focused on what needs we want to serve before we decide on what technology to deploy to fill those needs.

Because ultimately, customers are the very reason businesses exist. ~

Cecilia Boström is the User Experience Lead at Kollmorgen. She holds degrees in informatics and information technology from Gothenburg University and Chalmers University of Technology.

(ROBOT) EYES WIDE OPEN

Garrett Place

- Robotics Perception Leader at ifm -

Introduction

Put your hand over one eye. Now, try picking something up off the table or walking into the other room to get a glass of water. It is possible, but a bit more difficult than with both eyes. This simple act not only changes the way you see the world, but also how you interact with your environment.

Now, imagine both eyes are covered.

Most humans have the gift of seeing in three dimensions. This ability allows us to seamlessly interact with both structured and unstructured environments. It makes us that much more capable.

Until relatively recently, mobile robots did not possess this capability, condemning them to the most repeatable tasks in the most structured environments. Times have changed.

Automated Guided Vehicle (AGV) roaming a warehouse.

Past Barriers

Look at a mobile robot of the past, typically called an AGV (Automated Guided Vehicle), and you will see a large vehicle limited to the most repeatable tasks. One of the primary limitations of these vehicles was their inability to perceive their environment with the same richness we enjoy — in 3D.

There were methods to achieve autonomy back then. 2D LiDAR, ultrasonic, and radar sensors provided enough perception to allow safe, slow driving in one direction, with safety being vital. However, these systems lacked the granularity of pixels required to unlock full flexibility in application.

3D cameras were also available, promising to open the capabilities of the robot even further. While technically accurate, the size and cost of these cameras would drive up the overall entry price of these autonomous robots to a level that only the largest users could afford. The technology that promised to increase the capabilities of these robots was also responsible for pricing robots out of the market.

A dramatic shift would be required to open the capabilities of mobile robots without stifling their adoption.

Inflection Point

An inflection point is typically indicated by a dramatic change in a curve, an event, or series of events that symbolizes a significant, altering change. For robotic vision, that inflection point was the year of 2012.

It was during 2012 that three significant events took place, and these events created the current explosion of mobile robotics in logistics and manufacturing. They were:

1. The Microsoft launch of "Kinect for Windows"

Most had already "sniffed the wire" of this device well before 2012, attempting to find the magic key that would unlock point clouds from this $150 3D camera. However, this practice could not be official until Microsoft launched the SDK. The biggest benefactor of this event was higher education.

2. The release of "ROS by Example."

This seminal book made the Robot Operating System something that could be approached by experts and novices alike. Just a few months later in early 2013, OSRF would take over the maintenance of ROS while ROS-I was being founded. Again, the biggest benefactor was higher education.

The combination of these two events essentially democratized education on the use of point clouds in mobile and industrial robotics use cases.

Microsoft Xbox Kinect.

3. The Amazon purchase of Kiva Systems.

Amazon saw the potential of what this novel "Goods to Person" approach could bring to logistics and made the decision to take them off the market. However, they were not the only company that saw the potential and, as such, the purchase left quite a hole in the industry. It could be argued that almost every AMR company in business today was born after this event, mostly to fill the gap left by Kiva.

These three events truly changed the trajectory of the robotics industry. As with any dramatic change, the ripple effects were felt far and wide. New companies were pushing the envelope of what mobile robotics could achieve. At the same time, students were accelerating their learning of the use of 3D point clouds in robotics. This type of energy is what truly drove future innovation.

Push/Pull

Innovation in 3D imaging for mobile robotics started off slowly, considering the industry was moving fast as companies were focused on proving out their use cases. Most companies utilized what was readily available, making the Kinect one of the most widely used 3D cameras in the early days after the Kiva acquisition. Unfortunately, this did not last long as another M&A shifted the trajectory again when Apple bought PrimeSense, the Kinect technology company. This single event took the most widely available and affordable 3D camera off the market and led to a certain level of distrust in utilizing consumer technology for robotics use cases. More certainty was required for companies to move forward.

Fortunately, several industrial companies had already started promising 3D cameras that were "hardened" and provided supply chain certainty. As in the past, industrial housings and stable supply chains also brought larger size and more expense with them. However, these cameras provided enough of a runway to the industry to prove out their use cases and move to second and third generations of their platforms. Unfortunately, since they did not fix the cost problem facing the mobile robotics industry, these industrial 3D cameras could not be fully applied where needed.

A case of two steps forward, one step back. Changes in the price/performance ratio would be required to make 3D cameras ubiquitous on mobile robots.

Breaking the Price Barrier

Fortunately, the consumer industry again provided the spark for another round of innovation. The mobile phone industry, with its desire to push the capabilities of these devices, drove their technology partners to produce 3D cameras with tremendous capability at the lowest of costs. The potential volume in the market made this effort a reality.

These underlying technologies were then pushed into standalone camera systems that achieved the price/performance ratio needed by mobile robot companies for implementation. Finally, these companies could now apply the 3D camera technology required to increase the performance of their vehicles without dramatically increasing price. Mobile robots became more capable and more obtainable.

At this time, 3D cameras have become democratized.

The Next Challenge

Like the autonomous car industry, mobile robots must gain better situational awareness of their environment if their capabilities are to continue to grow. For AVs, this means providing a 360° view around the vehicle with the combination of 3D LiDAR, radar, 2D, and 3D camera systems. The mobile robot industry will see a similar architecture soon as prices for these technologies continue to decrease.

The challenge will then shift from one of price to one of integration. How do you seamlessly integrate datasets from different modalities in the same time scale and with the same availability? How do you do this with hardware from different suppliers? These technologies must be collaborative to achieve this goal, but all derive from different sources as of now.

Who is going to innovate in reducing the friction for integrating different sensing modalities into one wholistic dataset?

Data fusion will be the next barrier to overcome in mobile robotic perception. ~

Garrett Place is leading the 3D Perception Initiative for Mobile and Industrial Robots at ifm efector, inc.

CONSTRUCTION EMBRACES TECHNOLOGICAL CHANGE

Kaleb Steinhauer

- CEO of Genesis Dimensions -

In the year ahead, I expect emerging construction industry technologies will continue to mature, while the industry also makes a concerted effort to increase public awareness about new and emerging construction technologies. Companies will be spending a lot of time practicing and verifying their ideas to prove that a business case can exist.

The rocket ship for new construction technologies has launched and is en route to the moon, but it is a long journey and we are just barely underway. And a lack of technology may not even be the biggest hindrance to the adoption and use of new construction technology. The construction industry is complex and one of its biggest challenges is that there are a number of regulatory frameworks in which the industry needs to operate.

While the industry has been slow to embrace innovation, views on technology have begun to change over the last few years. Previously, innovative ideas were being discussed by companies far and wide, but many of them were simply pipe dreams.

Now, we are edging forward towards greater implementation of robotics and automation in everyday use. It is as if companies' innovative ideas have graduated elementary school and are now in junior high. They have not quite made it to all the way to high school yet.

Over the next year, we are likely to see people attempt to put their technology prototypes to work. They will push to validate their technologies to see if they might be commercially viable one day. Technology such as 3D printing used to be unheard of in construction, but it is now being discussed as a viable option. Other technologies will soon follow suit.

A lot of the focus in the next year for automation and robots in construction will be on overall awareness. It is not likely that a company will appear out of thin air to start 3D printing custom homes for people to live in. Instead, members of the public might see some viral videos that display cool, new, cutting-edge technology which may not be ready for mass commercialization.

These videos will build hype and help to increase the public's awareness and knowledge that transformative construction technologies are almost available.

However, the construction industry must be careful not to overpromise and under-deliver. If there is a lot of hype built up too early, people may be disappointed when it takes a while for the technology to appear in their lives.

Companies are working hard to make these technologies commercially available, but a lot must be accomplished in the next few years to make that a reality. The increased viability of prototypes has led to more investor dollars flowing into the space which has helped to push testing and development further.

Robots will be used in many ways for construction.

The U.S. Department of Defense is a big player in the industry and has started putting some serious money behind projects as they consider technologies that could be potential game changers for rapid deployment in conflict areas. At this point in time, almost every construction scale 3D printing company is dealing with the Department of Defense in one way or another.

Some of the challenges ahead will be proving that there is a legitimate business case for the technologies being developed. Early gantry-system based 3D printing technologies failed this test. While easier to design, they proved to be too large and unwieldy to be considered for widespread commercial adoption.

Construction technology systems need to be designed with business use cases in mind. If they can be successfully designed and implemented, the idea of being able to use these large machines for more precise applications has huge potential to impact all areas of robotics and automation.

Looking ahead, the next year will be heavily focused on verification of the technology. We have proven there is application, and we know there are interested end users. Now it is just about the final execution and then a push towards commercialization. This could take more than just the next year. It may be about 5 or so years before there is a proven commercial business case for 3D printing in construction, and not just technology that looks cool but is only capable of building a glorified hut.

As more money flows into the construction technology sector, companies will need to be careful with their financial management to maintain and extend runway, because it may take a while to prove they have correctly developed and tested their technologies. ~

Kaleb Steinhauer is the CEO of Genesis Dimensions. Kaleb's solution combines large-scale 3D printing and robotics to revolutionize the construction industry through lower labor costs and limited environmental impact.

COVID-19 PUSHES HOSPITALITY TOWARDS MORE AUTOMATION

Micah Green

- President and Founder of Maidbot -

2020 has been an extremely turbulent and unique year. COVID has had an unprecedented impact on the world and the impact will reverberate for years to come. This impact has rippled into every industry in the world — from hospitality to healthcare to commercial real estate. When looking at commercial real estate and hospitality, we begin focusing on the physical world where COVID has had a profound impact and has halted travel and tourism unlike any event before.

We have been forced to quarantine and that has drastically decreased travel and hotel occupancy rates around the world. Due to COVID, the expectation around the standard of cleanliness has gone up drastically. There is a greater push to minimize human-to-human interaction and socially distance — and operators are starting to rethink operations from ground zero.

The industry — as well as the public — want people to be able to travel, adventure, and play again. With these massive challenges, comes great opportunity. This is where robots come in and could help transform the landscape of our physical world — for the better.

Cleaning robots will be able to meet the requirements needed to reopen many elements of the physical world and bring us back closer to our prior understanding of 'normal.' Cleaning robots — from robot vacuums to scrubbers to disinfecting devices — will play instrumental roles in creating a new standard of cleanliness and safety that will redefine cleanliness moving forward. We will start to see new companies emerge from this opportunity and incumbent companies move uncomfortably fast to bring these technologies to reality. Let's explore the technologies and use cases that could be deployed.

Vacuuming

Although less obvious in terms of sanitization, automating vacuum cleaning for commercial spaces will be key in creating higher standards of cleanliness. In addition to the vacuum cleaning up debris and dust, it will also unlock time for cleaning staff members to focus on higher touch areas — from doorknobs to buttons and surfaces. Cleaning times have increased due to COVID, so anything that brings the time back down will help operators better manage their responsibilities.

Robot vacuuming could be deployed in hotel guestrooms and corridors as well as office spaces, assisted living facilities, apartment buildings, airports, and other spaces.

Rosie, a vacuuming robot, in a hotel guestroom.

Scrubbing

Floor surfaces can carry a lot of toxins and can even cultivate the spread of viruses which can attach to the soles of shoes. With this in mind, scrubbing will also be crucial for sanitizing spaces that have heavy foot traffic. Robots that can scrub the floors will help tackle a major area that is necessary to manage cleanliness in commercial real estate. An advantage of robots is that they clean consistently and can cover the entire area where humans may only cover a fraction of the space. Scrubbing robots are best suited for larger spaces such as shopping malls, retail stores, and airports.

Sanitization

Finally, to close the loop on floor cleaning robots and cleaning in general, sanitizing will be core to cleaning physical spaces in a COVID and post-COVID world. There are multiple methods to approach this problem including UVC lighting and liquids that can be sprayed onto surfaces by an electrostatic sprayer. Leveraging these solutions will enable operators to fully cover most of the responsibilities related to cleaning. Sanitization robots could be used in most spaces — especially in restaurants, stadiums, and hotels.

Although there are more tasks involved with commercial cleaning, vacuuming, scrubbing, and sanitizing will be core pillars when dealing with COVID. The public will also expect to see these practices implemented for the future — meaning these technologies will not lose value or demand after the vaccine is released.

Cleaning has traditionally been viewed as a back-of-house task that is often unnoticed. That said, with the impact of the virus, cleaning has been brought to the forefront of nearly everyone's minds — now a front of house focus. This is a catalyst for the implementation of robotics everywhere — especially in cleaning. Robots will truly be instrumental in building a cleaner and healthier world moving forward — and 2021 will just be the beginning. ~

Micah Estis Green is the Founder, President, and Chief Executive Officer of Maidbot, a robotics company on a mission to build robots to empower humans, starting with Rosie the robot.

MOBILE ROBOTICS AND SAFETY

Steven LaFevers

- VP of Emerging Technology at Hyster -

Building a Better Work Environment

Warehouse robotics are past the awareness stage. From horizontal transportation to storing and retrieving pallet loads at height, increasingly capable robotic solutions are becoming regular fixtures at warehousing and automation events, and in trade and business publications across the globe.[1,2,3,4]

And with technology advancing to become increasingly capable and scalable, the signals for greater adoption of robotic solutions are clear.

What better way to augment your labor pool, enable social distancing, boost productivity and improve retention than by automating repetitive, non-value-added tasks and focusing employees on more engaging, satisfying work?

The underlying industry forces make adopting robotics a pending reality, not just a possibility. Instead of building an understanding of robotic capabilities and their theoretical value, distribution center managers are asking for practical guidance to turn robotic ambition into adoption.

As with any new technology, safety is a critical element in this move to adoption, especially as so-called "cobotic" workflows feature humans working in close proximity to their robotic counterparts.

Person working in collaboration with an Automated Guided Vehicle (AGV).

Answering the question of safety on the path to adoption requires understanding robotic lift truck functionality, navigation behavior, and how their work can affect the roles of human counterparts — both in the normal course of business and in special circumstances.

Mobile Robotic Navigation Technology

While traditional automatic guided vehicles (AGVs) require guidance infrastructure like embedded wire, reflectors, or magnetic tape to navigate fixed pathways, the latest robotic lift trucks represent a departure from that paradigm. Today's robotic solutions are capable of moving through indoor logistics environments without navigation infrastructure or an operator.

This competency is made possible by Simultaneous Localization and Mapping (SLAM), in which robotic solutions use a reference map based on structural elements in the operating environment and compare it to what they sense in real time. This process allows the robotic lift truck solution to accurately and precisely self-locate — no additional navigation infrastructure required.

As know-how continues to mature and equipment decreases in cost, an increasingly popular navigation system is the laser-based technology, LiDAR — short for light detecting and ranging. This sensing method sends out pulses of laser light to determine the presence and distance of objects. To understand their location while in operation, mobile robotics use LiDAR to get the real time 'view' of surroundings, and then compare that to the reference map mentioned previously through the SLAM process.

Mobile Robots and Warehouse Safety

The consistent, strong performance of navigation technology and programming of site-specific rules enable robots to adapt to surroundings and real-time conditions while strictly following safety protocols. This capability helps reduce the risk of accidents, collisions, or other safety incidents, including when compared to lift trucks with human operators.

High turnover is common in warehousing, and with inexperience among operators comes increased risk.[5] OSHA estimates that approximately 20% to 25% of serious accidents involving powered industrial trucks are at least in part caused by inadequate training.[6] By comparison, robotic solutions deployed on the warehouse floor perform according to their programming from day one — without the extensive onboarding and training required to bring new operators to a satisfactory level of skill and experience.

While robots are predictable — they always follow safety procedures and can be programmed for site-specific rules of the road — people are not. And with humans working more frequently in close partnership with robots in what's known as cobotics, training everyone who enters the facility on how to safely interact with robots is especially important.

Mobile Robots and the Role of Workers

While it's clear that safety can get a leg-up, another chief advantage of robotics might not be as obvious. For some, the idea of robotic colleagues might conjure a bleak or even dystopian scene for modern workers, but the evidence suggests otherwise.

Automation technology can actually make work more "human" and make people happier at work. Academic research shows that organizations augmented by automation technologies are 33% more likely to be "human friendly" workplaces, in which employees are 31% more productive.[7] That's because robotics have the power to relieve workers of the monotony of repetitive tasks that are abundant in supply chain environments, so people can instead focus on more rewarding, higher responsibility work.

But delegating repetitive tasks to robotic solutions goes beyond busting boredom for employees, though it does that too. Enabling personnel to concentrate on more strategic work better equips them to remain focused and practice good judgment — both major advantages for warehouse safety and productivity.

Scientists have found that monotonous work can negatively impact mental health, cause major stress, and lead to burnout.[8] In her paper "Neuroscience Reveals That Boredom Hurts," Dr. Judy Willis, a neurologist and former classroom teacher, claims that when we're bored our judgment, goal-directed planning, risk assessment, focus, and control over emotions all suffer. [9]

For most workers, risk-assessment, focus, and judgment are a matter of performance. But for warehouse workers who spend their shifts supervising machinery, maneuvering heavy loads, and operating in a fast-paced environment, those factors are also fundamental to safe — and effective — operation.

As the conversation around employee engagement continues, robotics can play a part in shaping more meaningful work experiences. Improved job satisfaction is significant for individual employees, but it's also a boon to operations.

According to a GALLUP study, organizations with better employee engagement achieve higher performance, including substantially better retention, fewer accidents, and increased productivity.[10] Finding and training new hires can cost thousands, so using robotics to shift human workers toward responsibilities that help engage and retain them makes good business sense, too.[11]

Cobotics in Action

Through human-robot collaboration, cobotics capitalizes on the unfaltering reliability we expect from robots, and the knowledge, creativity, and decision-making skills of people. An example of a cobotic workflow in practice might include a worker who shifts her focus to picking and retrieving, assembling pallets, and other more complex, high-value tasks while an automated lift truck takes on the work of repeatedly traversing the warehouse, transporting product from point to point.

Spared from accompanying the lift truck, the worker invests more time completing high-impact tasks that both exercise and benefit from strategic thinking and problem solving. As the robotic lift truck fulfills needs throughout the facility, several features help it serve as a good steward of a safe working environment.

Automate Guided Vehicle navigates through a warehouse.

Robotic lift trucks adhere without exception to warehouse "rules of the road," such as maximum speed or minimum distance from pedestrians, other equipment, facility infrastructure and more. Where workers can be distracted by what they're carrying, co-workers, or environmental factors, robotic lift trucks are not prone to such diversions, as they rely on environmental sensors to detect and avoid obstacles.

Management software can direct robotic lift trucks to take predetermined routes to avoid heavy traffic areas. For operations with multiple robotic lift trucks in use, this ability to manage routes to help avoid bottlenecks is especially valuable, both for efficiency and safety.

A reduction in warehouse congestion can allow pedestrians and manned lift trucks to more easily navigate without delay or incident. That seamless traffic flow is especially valuable as warehouses ramp up storage capacity and order volumes during seasonal peaks and other demand fluctuations.

Special Circumstances: Worker Safety in a Pandemic

While robotic solutions offer significant operational benefits in the normal course of business, they've also been uniquely valuable during the COVID-19 pandemic.

As the outbreak unfolded, maintaining at least 6 feet of social distance between workers quickly became a critical measure to protect essential workers. Converting social distancing guidelines into reality required many operations to adjust workflows and reduce staffing levels, an added challenge as facilities worked to keep pace with surging consumer demand also brought on by the pandemic. Robots help operations respond to demand without increasing headcount, and they help reduce worker-to-worker contact that can risk virus transmission. For example, a robotic lift truck that transfers products between locations allows workers to remain relatively stationary or contained to a particular area as they work, helping maintain a safe social distance.

Introducing Robotics to a Warehouse

Advancements in underlying technologies have made robotics increasingly attractive. These technologies enable solutions that reliably practice facility traffic protocols, allowing them to drive productivity and work according to safety guidelines.

Though as with any warehouse tool, training workers on how to properly interact with them is just as essential.

Once employees are thoroughly trained on proper protocol for working in cobotic settings, putting robotics to work in your warehouse can also help provide a more nuanced benefit — freeing workers to focus on roles that keep them more mindful and engaged. ~

ENDNOTES

1. https://www.supplychainbrain.com/articles/30998-on-location-at-modex-2020-the-state-of-robotics
2. https://www.automateshow.com/conference/automate-2019-conference-agenda/
3. https://www.dcvelocity.com/articles/44254-driverless-forklifts-are-now-a-thing
4. https://www.bloomberg.com/opinion/articles/2019-10-04/jobs-data-robots-are-catching-up-to-humans-in-workforce
5. https://www.bls.gov/news.release/jolts.t16.htm
6. https://www.osha.gov/laws-regs/federalregister/1995-03-14
7. https://www.prnewswire.com/news-releases/automation-is-making-work-more-human-global-research-reveals-300714154.html
8. https://pubmed.ncbi.nlm.nih.gov/2714928/
9. https://journals.sagepub.com/doi/abs/10.1177/003172171409500807?journalCode=pdka&
10. https://news.gallup.com/poll/241649/employee-engagement-rise.aspx
11. https://www.peoplekeep.com/blog/employee-retention-the-real-cost-of-losing-an-employee

Steven LaFevers is Vice President of emerging technology for Hyster Company. He is responsible for the growth and profitability of the organization's comprehensive offering of technology-driven products and services that accompany materials handling equipment investments. These emerging technology solutions include market-leading innovations in robotics and automation, motive power, and telematics.

MANAGING PROJECTS IN A TECHNOLOGY-CENTERED WORLD

Nawfal Patel

- Operations Manager of The Futurist Institute -

Project management has been changing rapidly over the past decade as new technologies allow for more automation throughout various phases in a project's life cycle. In the year ahead, I expect project managers to increasingly leverage technologies to their advantage to simplify and expedite the project management process.

The fact that more and more companies use agile planning strategies combined with a potential large-scale shift towards permanent remote workers will only increase the opportunities for project managers to utilize technology to their benefit.

The project management process is long and detail oriented. A lot of documentation is produced throughout to keep track of exactly what is happening on a project and why.

It is critical for project managers to utilize technology to help keep themselves and their teams organized throughout the various phases. Using platforms like monday or Upwork can help to automate a lot of the smaller, easily controlled aspects of the process.

Monday is an all-in-one project management software that can help streamline your team's workflow so that contributors can focus on high impact activities and everyone can see how the project is progressing in one centralized location. Upwork can help automate contracts and invoicing for freelancers on your team which removes a very time-consuming activity off the team leader's desk.

Of course, there is also the ability to use cloud-based sharing applications like Dropbox, box, and Google Drive that allow for greater team coordination and improved version control, which can help reduce the risk that teammates lose track of deliverables or the status of workstreams.

Project managers need to leverage technologies like this to make sure they can complete their projects on time and within budget, especially as the landscape of remote work evolves rapidly.

Effectively communicating what is going on and how things are changing in a variable environment is one of the most critical parts of being a project manager. The COVID-19 pandemic has clearly shown how important being a good communicator is with regard to project management.

With more and more people working remotely, project managers who are used to their team being co-located have had to adapt. Online tools like Trello or Asana can be extremely useful in helping keep everyone on the same page. And still other teams use Slack or Whatsapp.

Some teams that are used to being co-located and using visual tools like Kanban boards to visually track activity progress and milestones may like using Trello to digitally track how a project is progressing.

Developing an efficient communications plan with the technology available will become an increasingly prevalent part of project management as leaders work to keep all team members working efficiently and focused on the overall goals of a project.

Another important part of project management is quality control. Quality control focuses on making sure a project's deliverables are produced in accordance with guidelines set in the project management plan which were agreed upon with the sponsor. Technology can be leveraged throughout the quality control process in various ways to help expedite and control the tasks at hand.

Some companies with especially time sensitive projects have begun to use employee monitoring systems to see how effective and efficient their workers are while working from home. This is a trend that is also likely to increase in the future.

After all, if a worker's production quality is dropping while working from home, then it will be up to the project manager to identify the source of the problem and work with the team member to resolve the issue.

Technology will be key to working through quality issues such as this since co-locating may not be a viable option for the next year.

Looking forward, building effective teams will become more and more difficult as people continue to work remotely, and projects may even be started and completed without team members ever being co-located.

It will be up to a project manager to adapt in differing circumstances and build team camaraderie which can help generate buy-in to the overall success of the project. Project managers will have to rely on interpersonal skills and utilize co-working technologies to figure out how to get a team to perform at its best if they do not have the ability to interact face to face.

The COVID-19 pandemic has been a catalyst to fundamentally alter how many businesses manage their operations and complete their projects.

Looking ahead to the post-pandemic world in which a vaccine seems likely to come to fruition in the year ahead, the core parts of project management will remain the same as detailed process planning, effective and efficient communication, and quality control will all still be critical to project success.

But even with prospects of a vaccine, workers are likely to continue working remotely at much greater levels than they had before the COVID-19 pandemic.

As teams become more dispersed in 2021 and projects become more complex, I believe project managers will increasingly rely on technologies to help them keep their team members informed of critical information, automate controlled parts of the project management process, and complete their projects on schedule and within budget. ~

Nawfal Patel is the Operations Manager of The Futurist Institute and has managed a variety of projects focused on technology and financials trends while operating in very remote locations as well as on site. Nawfal is a Certified Futurist and Long-Term Analyst™ holding the FLTA™ designation. He also holds the Project Management Professional (PMP) designation.

INVESTING IN NATIONAL SECURITY HUMAN CAPITAL

Jacob Sotiriadis

- Chief USAF Strategic Foresight and Futures Branch -

The need for technological preparedness, adaptability, and agility will underpin the future of national security entities. These are the same requirements that every organization — private sector, government, defense, and NGO — must meet to thrive in 2021 and beyond.

On the upside, technology presents tremendous potential for operational leverage in national security and intelligence. We should note, however, that the national security establishment is also not immune to job displacement resulting from heightened automation. Military and intelligence organizations must carefully consider how to balance human capital requirements with integrating disruptive tech solutions. A lack of preparedness today could disadvantage operational performance tomorrow.

There are two critical ways to mitigate these risks. First, organizations must adjust and augment skillsets to match the rate of change in technology — both digital and physical. Additionally, (and perhaps more importantly) leaders must scope the requirements of new roles and create new jobs/positions designed to leverage technological upside potential. This is not merely about jobs being replaced by automation. Rather, there is a real, growing need to align new requirements and capabilities with tech solutions that may yield entirely new skill sets.

A Military Intelligence Problem

Technology will accelerate change, support analytical scale, reduce manpower footprints, and streamline existing processes. We are observing these trends today in the form of rapid information processing and an acceleration of networked effects. Nonetheless, there is also a cautionary tale here — no digital transformation will be complete without addressing cognitive deficits.

Technology is just one critical piece for effective national security strategies.

Consider, for example, that today there may be dozens of human analysts focused on any particular intelligence area.

As technological leverage increases, it will be easier to aggregate and analyze more data and quicker than ever before. This is automation's potential to augment labor-intensive, human capital work. But while the ability to access more information and more data will increase exponentially, it will not reduce the need for human-contextualized problem-solving. In fact, with greater access to data, there will be an ever-greater need for more problem-solving skills and greater depth of analysis.

Leveraging technology represents more than possessing physical technologies and automation. It is not simply about a digital transformation. The keys to future success in this area are the integration of all physical and digital technological capabilities available with adaptive, cognitive abilities.

How can organizations address both digital and cognitive deficits? In order to strike the right balance, organizations must implement a culture catalyst element. Completing this equation, futures-based thinking can help broaden and deepen strategic planning in the face of exponential uncertainties. This is one means to address how to best integrate future tech solutions and work requirements while preparing organizations to face a range of outcomes.

By expanding the range of possible futures, organizations can learn how to adapt and change — even when the signals of tomorrow may seem far-fetched today.

Networking Forces and Cognitive Operating Systems

In 2021 and beyond, military and national security entities will be consumed with networking their forces and trading in the currency of information and data. This means instantaneous sharing of information and data that enables a decision advantage within a rapidly shifting security environment.

Digital connectivity alone, however, will not be enough to prevail on tomorrow's battlefields or in tomorrow's boardrooms. The solution to maximizing human capital lies in creating, enhancing, and developing our cognitive operating system.

Here, we refer to a disciplined way of:
1.) Questioning our assumptions.
2.) Seeing the inter-connectivity of events.
3.) Embracing analytic complexity in our strategic planning.

Doing so requires both crafting and proliferating better methodologies for anticipatory thinking. Futures strategies are critical to helping analysts as well as leaders and decision-makers flex these critical muscles at the individual and the command level more broadly.

Recommendations — Intentional Strategies

In a world of increasing technological disruption, we cannot focus on fighting the previous war. We must embrace the opportunities and risks that new technologies present — and we must find a way to think beyond historical limitations.

Digital solutions are necessary — but not sufficient — for success in retaining decision advantage. Seizing and occupying the cognitive high ground in the national security arena is more than just "buying things," developing weapons systems, or increasing technological leverage. It is also ensuring that professionals are given powerful technological tools with the requisite cognitive capacity for sense-making.

2020 was a critical year for digital transformation across all sectors. But make no mistake — 2021 will be a year when companies seek increasingly innovative means to derive value chains from technology. It will be a year in which intentional strategies are indispensable to achieving success.

In national security, defense, and the corporate world, organizations cannot simply "stumble" into tech solutions (as was the case in many instances in 2020). Absent a deliberate strategy and a clear road map for implementation, even the most advanced or disruptive technologies will not be a panacea. In the world of national security, resource management will be increasingly critical — and making efficient choices will be a hallmark of success.

Finally, organizations will increasingly emphasize the ROI for activities and investments — especially in defense and security. Ensuring that resources are efficiently allocated in the year ahead and beyond will require not only an efficient approach, but also an intentional integration of physical technologies, digital technologies, and human capital to maintain decision advantage.

While one can never completely mitigate uncertainty, harnessing the power of futures thinking will allow organizations in the public and private sectors to address their respective challenges and adversaries in a range of scenarios. ~

Disclaimer: The views expressed in this essay are those of the author and do not reflect the official policy or position of the U.S. Air Force, Department of Defense, or the U.S. Government.

Lt. Col. Jacob Sotiriadis is the Chief of the Strategic Foresight and Futures Branch of the U.S. Air Force. He holds a PhD in political science with a focus on futures studies from the University of Hawai'i at Mānoa.

THE HINGE FACTOR IN DIGITAL DEXTERITY

Robert Handfield

- Professor at NC State University and Author -

If unrestricted information flow is so important for effective decision-making, then why does it seem so difficult to make it happen? What prevents information from getting to the right people who make the decisions? And how do we even know whether an organization is effectively utilizing data to make predictions on flows in order to develop a competitive advantage over those in the same market?

The answer lies in the extent of an organization's dexterity and sophistication in employing data and in its cultural embrace of digital capabilities. Data in and of itself is not a definitive advantage. Data is, of course, everywhere — and most organizations are overwhelmed by it.

The key to predicting flows is not data, but knowledge. Specifically, it's the ability and action of the human-machine interaction to drive changes in a systems design (and flows).[1] Information is not knowledge, and data residing in an organization are not knowledge either.

Data which is spread and configured in a manner which allows prediction occurs through the carriers of knowledge: *individuals.* With this in mind, we can begin to understand how the so-called "digital transformation" of an organization occurs not through its data and information technologies, but in the degree of "digital dexterity" of individuals in that organization.

Digital dexterity is widely promoted by consultants and think-tanks. But what does it mean?

Relatively few managers we've spoken with have been able to effectively define it. More importantly, few know how to recognize it in an organization, or how to help its employees develop it.

Gartner, a business research and analysis firm, coined "digital dexterity" in response to the notion that the digital component of most jobs is increasing. Craig Roth, a research vice president at Gartner, defined digital dexterity as "the ability and ambition to use technology for better business outcomes."[2] Business models increasingly depend on the digital dexterity of the workforce to use technology to drive digital transformation goals.

The key element of any new tech project, product rollout, or change in the way things are done is a workforce's willingness to fully engage with new technology, adapt their work style to include it, and quickly learn how it fits into the overall mission of an organization.

Helen Poitevin, a vice president and analyst at Gartner, noted, "Business and IT leaders need to employ the right talent with a specific set of mindsets, beliefs and behaviors — which we call digital dexterity — to launch, finish and capitalize on digital initiatives." Digital dexterity, she said, is less about tech skills and more about "a specific set of mindsets, beliefs and behaviors."

An important question to ask regarding human-machine interaction is: Where does human decision-making enter the loop? A very interesting book that helped us think through this concept is *How Chance and Stupidity Have Changed History: The Hinge Factor* by Erik Durschmied.[3]

The author looks at battles that changed the course of history, including the Crusaders' loss of the cross to Muslim forces at the Battle of Hattin in 1187, the defeat of the French at the Battle of Agincourt in 1415, Napoleon's defeat at Waterloo in 1815, and the battle of Antietam in 1862.

Each of these defeats was caused by a blunder, the caprice of weather, or individual incompetence. These unforeseeable errors resulted in the loss of thousands of lives and changed the course of history.

We believe that such a "hinge factor" also occurs in supply chains, when an individual leader must make a critical difficult decision in the face of uncertainty and limited intelligence, and with significant resources at play.

A blunder made at such times can have incredible follow-on effects on an organization's future.

What is the "hinge factor" in supply chains? We've explored more and more organizations that are developing global security operations centers, which show incredible amounts of real-time data. One of these we saw at Flex, another at Caterpillar, and yet another at Biogen, in which a "control room" shows activities occurring around the world. Huge maps in these rooms show events such as flooding in India, riots in Hong Kong, and forest fires in California, as well as other disruptions.

Resilinc developed a risk platform to help its customers stay abreast of global events which might affect its supply chain. This platform can also link an event to key suppliers within a range of the geographic location, and, through a bill of materials, identify the financial impact of an event.

What managers do with this information is not prescribed; managers who gravitate to systems like Resilinc must know how to respond when alerted to a risk event. This is the real hinge factor in supply chain: when is a risk event a "false alarm" that should be ignored, or when should action be taken by managers?

Consider 9/11, when the chief air controller of the FAA realized that the U.S. was under attack. His immediate response was to ground all flights, including those in the air. Rob was on a flight from Detroit to Moline, Ill., that day. He ended up being deposited in Kalamazoo MI, and had to drive home to North Carolina in a rental car.

In retrospect, grounding planes was an enormously impactful, courageous call, and it turned out to be the right one. But we don't always have the benefit of hindsight when we are called on to make quick decisions when confronted with risky events.

The benefit of risk management systems (like Resilinc) is that they provide managers with an early warning — the key in the battlefield of supply chain management. When you can get information ahead of your competitor, your company can move its assets more efficiently and win the battle.

This is a real benefit *only* if we use the information to make the right call. But too many "false alarms" can be costly if it requires an "all hands on deck" approach every time. Hence, prudence must be balanced with careful consideration of the facts to avoid recklessness or abandon or ignorance of the facts.

For example, the rain that fell on the ploughed ground at the battle of Agincourt didn't halt the attack of the superior French army.[4] Ignoring the fact that the battleground had become a muddy mess, they drove in their cavalry, loaded with heavily armored knights.

When the horses fell, mired in mud, English longbowmen massacred the French, whose army had ten times more men. Similarly, poor communication and a lack of critical supplies (in this case, a fistful of nails) led to Napoleon's defeat at Waterloo in 1815. In the same manner, supply chain leaders when facing a risk event need to carefully plan ahead to establish how they will react to unexpected risks, including hurricanes, terrorist attacks, cyber terrorism, and yes, slow-moving pandemics.

It will be important in the future to continue to explore how the combination of automation, digital technology, and human decision-making can align to improve a variety of decisions within global supply chains.

The combination of these factors, which we call digital dexterity, provides "speed-to-value" when applied to a number of supply chain situations. Applied digital dexterity will face barriers that can hinder even the most careful evolutionary design, blocking supply chain flow. Most involve human error: the managerial mindset to "CYA", poor decision-making skills, lack of data analytic skills, or in many cases, a reluctance to adapt to changing conditions.

These barriers prevent the ideal future state, characterized by managers able to employ data to predict flows of materials, people, demand, risk, or any other attribute important to supply chains. ~

ENDNOTES

1. Bejan, 2016, p 16.
2. https://www.gartner.com/en/newsroom/press-releases/2019-09-17-gartner-says-the-cio-is-the-culture-change-agent-to-augment-digital-dexterity-in-the-workplace
3. Durschmied, Erik. *How Chance and Stupidity Have Changed History: The Hinge Factor* Hodder & Stoughton; New Ed edition (May 23, 2013).
4. Ibid.

Robert Handfield is the Executive Director of the North Carolina State University's Supply Chain Resource Cooperative. The SCRC is a university-industry partnership dedicated to advancing the supply chain industry and the professionalism of its practitioners.

RETURNING TO THE ROAD MAP

Daniel Stanton
- President of SecureMarking -

Jason Schenker
- Chairman of The Futurist Institute -

Overview

In a frenzied and frenetic attempt to rapidly bridge the chasm of digital transformation ushered in by COVID-19, something got missed. This isn't to say that the move into technological solutions was one of impetuous folly.

After all, there is a reason why automation and digital connectivity had heretofore lurched rather than leapt forward. So, perhaps more care could have been taken to ensure the leap forward could have been sustained. But the immediate needs of the pandemic afforded corporate strategists no such luxury.

Now, looking into 2021, the future faces bifurcated dynamics. On the one hand, there is likely to be a persistently elevated level of stress on e-commerce supply chains long after vaccinations are widely available and de rigueur.

This is where the challenges in 2021 begin, with a retrenching of operations — as a response to these pressures. This is the other hand of the bifurcation emerging in the year ahead.

If 2020 was the year of rapidly cobbling supply chain systems and operations together to meet critical demands, 2021 is likely to be the year of perfecting and streamlining. If you've ever heard the phrase, "Do it bad, then do it better," then you've already heard the mantra that will dominate the automation Zeitgeist in the year ahead.

This isn't to say 2020 was bad. But for all companies in the supply chain, automation, and material handling worlds, 2021 will the year to do everything better.

Building Blocks
Every supply chain is comprised of three primary elements: people, process, and technology.

While technology has become a more important lever of supply chain capacity in recent years, the COVID-19 pandemic revealed the potential for technology to also protect people. This isn't just an issue of contactless capabilities that reduced human contact to combat the spread of COVID-19. It was also about making sure the supply chain could be resilient in the face of surging demand.

Despite the pressures exerted, the supply chain did not break. And that was because of the technology we have. And it should now be clear that robots make supply chains resilient — even in the face of pandemic. More automation means more resilience.

Risk Management Considerations

With a full-throttle push into automation, there are risks. Increasing the number of devices and connectivity increases cybersecurity risks by expanding the potential attack surface of a company's operations. Plus, there are often operational blind spots, and there's also the not insignificant possibility to miss some of the details of implementing automated solutions. The needs for backup systems, failsafe and failover systems, and other operational controls are critical.

The best way to address risk management is to adopt a culture of risk by embedding risk management across organizations. Risk management often justifies risk management, but automation, robots, and AI are not inherently riskless. There may be tradeoffs in these risks. It is this shifting of risks that needs to be understood to maximize operational sustainability and resilience in the face of new risks.

Value of People in a World of Automation

Despite the push toward more technology, people will remain a critical part of the supply chain. In fact, the demands on those people are likely to become more sophisticated and significant.

This is especially true when it comes to supplier relationships. In fact, there could even be an increased demand for customer service attentiveness. Of course, that could help increase stickiness of customer relationships, but it will require effort. After all, there is no substitute for strong business relationships. And there will be new needs for those relationships in the future.

Making Sure Solutions Fully Deliver

In the rush to provide solutions against the backdrop of the COVID-19 pandemic, there has been a rush to acquire technologies. But often this was done without a roadmap. Yet, without a roadmap and a plan, acquiring even best-of-breed technologies often falls short.

Without having a plan in advance, the risk of making inefficient choices, ineffective choices, and unintegrated choices rises. Without a proper implementation, solutions these technologies promise won't fully deliver. For companies that did not adopt or acquire technologies with the full intentionality of a road map, 2021 will be a year to revisit their goals and technologies, to try and make them align for the greatest chance of success in a world that struggles to move past the COVID pandemic.

Any additional investments required should be evaluated in a less frenzied backdrop in a way that strategically balances value and investments, including short-term needs and ROI as well as long-term road map integration.

Capturing Big Opportunities

Ensuring companies derive value from their technological investments is the primary conditio sine qua non. But while there is a need to seek balance in the wake of the COVID-19 pandemic, the opportunities presented by COVID-19 don't come along every year. This means that despite all the disruptions and negative impacts of COVID-19, there has been a truly unique chance for companies to make long-term changes and investments.

But robots are not a panacea.

They represent an opportunity for supply chain businesses and industries. This is why it is important to tie up loose ends in the year ahead and return to a strategic road map, in order to make sure those opportunities are not lost.

Still, there is a balance to strike. And even though companies need to shore up their positions, address risks, and find new ways to lever their people, they should continue to embrace unique opportunities to lead transformation today — but also to plant the seeds of long-term impact for tomorrow. ~

Daniel Stanton is a supply chain entrepreneur, the best-selling author of *Supply Chain Management for Dummies*, and a popular LinkedIn Learning instructor. He is also the President of SecureMarking.

Jason Schenker is the Chairman of The Futurist Institute and the editor of this almanac. He lives in Austin, Texas, with his wife, Ashley, and their dog, Mister O's.

THE FUTURIST INSTITUTE

 THE FUTURIST INSTITUTE

The Futurist Institute was founded in 2016 to help analysts, executives, and professionals incorporate technology and trend risks and opportunities into strategic planning. The Futurist Institute confers the Futurist and Long-Term Analyst™ (FLTA) designation and helps analysts become Certified Futurists™. Our courses have been approved for continuing education hours by the Certified Financial Planner Board of Standards (CFP Board).

Current Courses

The Future After COVID
The Future of Work
The Future of Data
The Future of Energy
The Future of Finance
The Future of Healthcare
The Future of Leadership
The Future of Transportation
Futurist Fundamentals
Quantum Computing
Write the Future

Visit The Futurist Institute:
www.futuristinstitute.org

ABOUT THE EDITOR

Mr. Schenker is the President of Prestige Economics and Chairman of The Futurist Institute. He has been ranked one of the most accurate financial forecasters and futurists in the world. Bloomberg News has ranked Mr. Schenker a top forecaster in 44 categories, including #1 in the world for his accuracy in 26 categories, including for his forecasts of the Euro, the British Pound, the Russian Ruble, the Chinese RMB, crude oil prices, natural gas prices, gold prices, industrial metals prices, agricultural commodity prices, and U.S. jobs.

Mr. Schenker's work has been featured in *The Wall Street Journal*, *The New York Times*, and the *Frankfurter Allgemeine Zeitung*. He has appeared on CNBC, CNN, ABC, NBC, MSNBC, Fox, Fox Business, BNN, Bloomberg Germany, and the BBC. Mr. Schenker has also been a guest host of Bloomberg Television, and he is a contributor for *Bloomberg Opinion*. Mr. Schenker was ranked one of the top 100 most influential financial advisors in the world by Investopedia in 2018.

Mr. Schenker attends OPEC and Fed events, and he has given keynotes for private companies, public corporations, industry groups, and the U.S. Federal Reserve. He has advised NATO and the U.S. government on the future of work, blockchain, Bitcoin, cryptocurrency, quantum computing, data analysis, forecasting, and fake news. Mr. Schenker has written 30 books. Twelve have been bestsellers, including: *The Future After COVID*, *Jobs for Robots*, *Quantum: Computing Nouveau*, *Commodity Prices 101*, *Recession-Proof*, *Futureproof Supply Chain*, *Electing Recession*, *The Future of Finance is Now*, *The Future of Energy*, *The Dumpster Fire Election*, and *The Robot and Automation Almanac* for 2018 and 2020. Mr. Schenker also wrote *The Promise of Blockchain*, *Futureproof Supply Chain*, *The Future of Food and Agriculture*, *The Fog of Data*, *Financial Risk Management Fundamentals*, *Midterm Economics*, *Spikes: Growth Hacking Leadership*, *Strategic Cost-Cutting*, *Strategic Cost-Cutting After COVID*, and *Reading the Economic Tea Leaves*. Mr. Schenker was featured as one of the world's foremost futurists in *After Shock*. His futurist research was included in an unclassified Pentagon report in June 2020.

Mr. Schenker advises executives, industry groups, institutional investors, and central banks as the President of Prestige Economics. He also founded The Futurist Institute, for which he created a rigorous course of study that includes The Future of Work, The Future of Transportation, The Future of Data, The Future of Finance, Futurist Fundamentals, The Future of Energy, The Future of Leadership, The Future of Healthcare, The Future of Quantum Computing, and The Future After COVID. Mr. Schenker is also an instructor for LinkedIn Learning courses on Economic Indicators, Risk Management, Audit and Due Diligence, and Recession-Proof Strategies.

Mr. Schenker holds a Master's in Applied Economics from UNC Greensboro, a Master's in Negotiation, Conflict Resolution, and Peacebuilding from CSU Dominguez Hills, a Master's in Germanic Languages and Literature from UNC Chapel Hill, and a Bachelor's in History and German from The University of Virginia. He also holds a Certificate in FinTech from MIT, a Certificate in Supply Chain Management from MIT, a Certificate in Professional Development from UNC, a Certificate in Negotiation from Harvard Law School, a Certificate in Cybersecurity from Carnegie Mellon, and a Professional Certificate in Strategic Foresight from the University of Houston. Mr. Schenker holds the designations CMT® (Chartered Market Technician), and CFP® (Certified Financial Planner). He is also a Certified Futurist and Long-Term Analyst™ and holds the FLTA™ designation.

Before founding Prestige Economics, Mr. Schenker worked as a Risk Specialist at McKinsey and Company, where he provided content direction to trading, risk, and commodity project teams on six continents. Prior to McKinsey, Mr. Schenker was the Chief Energy and Commodity Economist at Wachovia, which is now Wells Fargo.

Based in Austin, Texas, Mr. Schenker is one of only 100 CEOs on the Texas Business Leadership Council, a non-partisan organization that advises Texas elected leadership at the state and federal level. Mr. Schenker is a Governance Fellow of the National Association of Corporate Directors. He also sits on multiple boards and is the VP of Finance on the Executive Committee of The Texas Lyceum, the preeminent non-partisan leadership group in Texas. Mr. Schenker is also a member of the Bretton Woods Committee.

PUBLISHER

Prestige Professional Publishing was founded in 2011 to produce insightful and timely professional reference books. We are registered with the Library of Congress.

Published Titles

Be the Shredder, Not the Shred
Commodity Prices 101
Electing Recession
Financial Risk Management Fundamentals
Futureproof Supply Chain
A Gentle Introduction to Audit and Due Diligence
Jobs for Robots
Jobs for Robots: COVID Edition
Midterm Economics
Quantum: Computing Nouveau
Reading the Economic Tea Leaves
Recession-Proof Career Strategies After COVID
Robot-Proof Yourself
Spikes: Growth Hacking Leadership
Strategic Cost-Cutting
Strategic Cost-Cutting After COVID
The Dumpster Fire Election
The Economics of Revolt and Revolution
The Fog of Data
The Future After COVID
The Future of Agriculture
The Future of Energy

PUBLISHER

Published Titles

The Future of Finance is Now
The Future of Food and Agriculture After COVID
The Promise of Blockchain
Write the Future
The Robot and Automation Almanac - 2018
The Robot and Automation Almanac - 2019
The Robot and Automation Almanac - 2020
The Robot and Automation Almanac - 2021

Forthcoming Titles

After the COVID Vaccine
Content Monster
Disruption Warfare
The Future of Healthcare
The Future of Marketing
The Future of Travel and Leisure

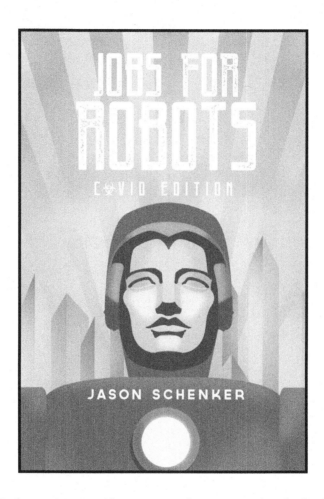

Jobs for Robots: COVID Edition provides an in-depth look at the future of automation and robots, with a focus on opportunities and risks for the future following the COVID-19 pandemic. The first edition of *Jobs for Robots* was published in February 2017. It has been a #1 Best Seller on Amazon.

In *The Future After COVID*, top-ranked forecaster and Chairman of The Futurist Institute Jason Schenker offers a futurist perspective into the potential long-term changes, challenges, and opportunities that COVID-19 is likely to have for over a dozen different critical fields and industries. The book was published in April 2020. This book has been an international bestseller.

DISCLAIMER

FROM THE PUBLISHER

The following disclaimer applies to any content in this book:

This book is commentary intended for general information use only and is not investment advice. Prestige Professional Publishing LLC does not make recommendations on any specific or general investments, investment types, asset classes, unregulated markets, specific equities, bonds, or other investment vehicles. Prestige Professional Publishing LLC does not guarantee the completeness or accuracy of analyses and statements in this book, nor does Prestige Professional Publishing LLC assume any liability for any losses that may result from the reliance by any person or entity on this information. Opinions, forecasts, and information are subject to change without notice. This book does not represent a solicitation or offer of financial or advisory services or products; this book is only market commentary intended and written for general information use only. This book does not constitute investment advice.

DISCLAIMER

FROM THE FUTURIST INSTITUTE

The following disclaimer applies to any content in this book:

This book is commentary intended for general information use only and is not investment advice. The Futurist Institute does not make recommendations on any specific or general investments, investment types, asset classes, non-regulated markets, specific equities, bonds, or other investment vehicles. The Futurist Institute does not guarantee the completeness or accuracy of analyses and statements in this book, nor does The Futurist Institute assume any liability for any losses that may result from the reliance by any person or entity on this information. Opinions, forecasts, and information are subject to change without notice. This book does not represent a solicitation or offer of financial or advisory services or products, and are market commentary intended and written for general information use only. This book does not constitute investment advice.

Prestige Professional Publishing, LLC
4412 City Park Road #4
Austin, Texas 78730
www.prestigeprofessionalpublishing.com

ISBN: 978-1-946197-68-9 *Paperback*
      978-1-946197-71-9 *Ebook*

FI THE FUTURIST INSTITUTE

Made in the USA
Monee, IL
11 December 2020

52256759R00105